THE ECO SMALLHOLDING

Planning and Designing for Sustainability

MICHAEL LITTLEWOOD

THE ECO SMALLHOLDING

Published by

Ecodesignscape
Hinton St. George,
Somerset TA17 8SD

Disclaimer
Whilst every effort has been made to ensure that the contents of this book are accurate and as up to date as possible, neither the publisher nor the author can be held responsible for any consequence arising from the use of information contained herein. Neither can we be held liable for any errors or omissions that may have occurred in the book or for any work carried out by any individual or company.

ISBN: 978-0-9955201-0-3

Edited by Gaby Bartai

Designed by Andrew Crane

Printed and bound in the UK by PublishPoint
from KnowledgePoint Limited, Reading.

Cover illustration by David Calow

CONTENTS

Foreword 7

Introduction 9

1 The principles of eco-farming

Sustainability 15

Ecological design 15

Organic methods 17

Diversification 18

Eco-friendly options 18

Aesthetics 19

2 Essential elements

Scale and size 21

Design elements 23

3 Planning for success

The benefits of planning 37

Who should produce the plan? 40

A management plan 41

4 Aims and requirements

Aspirations 49

Personal resources 52

Smallholding selection 54

5 Survey

Site description 59

Maps and plans 63

Research 67

6 Analysis

Evaluation 75

Objectives 80

7 Design

Designing with nature 83

Connections, zones and sectors 85

Layouts 91

8 Implementation

The work plan 97

Budgeting and resources 100

Monitoring and review 101

9 Conclusion 103

10 Case studies

The Birches 105

Wandale 113

Troutwells 119

Appendices

1. Landscape elements 124

2. Zone systems 129

3. Habitats for wildlife 130

4. Ecology drawing 132

Information

Further reading 134

Resources 135

Acknowledgements 136

Conversion tables 137

About the author 139

FOREWORD

Owning and running a smallholding is an increasingly attractive prospect for more of us as our world becomes ever faster-paced and divorced from the natural rhythms of Mother Earth. Our own slice of paradise promises the chance to get closer to the land, to raise and grow healthy, nutritious food, and to reconnect with a simpler, happier way of life.

It's a romantic thought, but success depends on meticulous planning. Hours spent planning will save many days, weeks and even years of hard work. By taking a calm and measured approach to your new venture, it will undoubtedly thrive.

Central to the ethos of the eco-smallholding is working with the natural assets on site – the flowers, trees and wildlife that make your smallholding home. Putting wildlife as core to what you do, rather than a mere afterthought, will bring untold benefits. Research proves that far from 'wasting' land, natural features and strips of land dedicated to conservation actually boost overall productivity, saving you time and money while ensuring truly organic, wholesome food. An eco-smallholding isn't a 'nice-to-have', it just makes plain old common sense!

This book burrows into the intricacies of eco-smallholding planning, guiding you through the basics so that you can lay the foundations for a healthy holding that works for you and your family, the local community and, of course, the planet. Planning is the key to success. You have the enthusiasm to get started – now let Michael share his many years of experience and genuine passion so you can make a real go of it.

Benedict Vanheems MSc, gardening and wildlife writer

INTRODUCTION

THERE IS NOW CONSIDERABLE CONCERN for the rural environment, and particularly about the methods of farming practised over the last 70 years. Modern industrial farming has created a countryside in crisis, taking its toll on rural communities, wildlife, animal husbandry, the quality of food and the landscape. Yet – especially on a small acreage – it is possible to farm on an ecological basis which is sustainable, diversified, and causes no long-term or irreversible environmental changes. Small-scale farming can be socially, ethically and aesthetically acceptable, while still being economically viable. The key to harmonising these apparently competing demands is careful planning and design.

Only two or three generations ago, most farms were relatively small mixed holdings, producing both livestock and crops. This allowed the rotation of different crops and animals around the fields, which maintained soil fertility and kept diseases in check. Today, most farms are large specialist units growing just a few crops, or keeping one type of livestock, so chemicals are needed to maintain fertility and prevent disease.

In the name of 'efficiency', energy-hungry machinery has replaced the majority of the workers that a farm used to support. This has radically altered the appearance of the countryside, with the creation of vast fields and the loss of hedges and woodlands. It has also had a huge impact on the rural population. Until the mid-20th century, farms were managed in a way that brought benefits to the whole

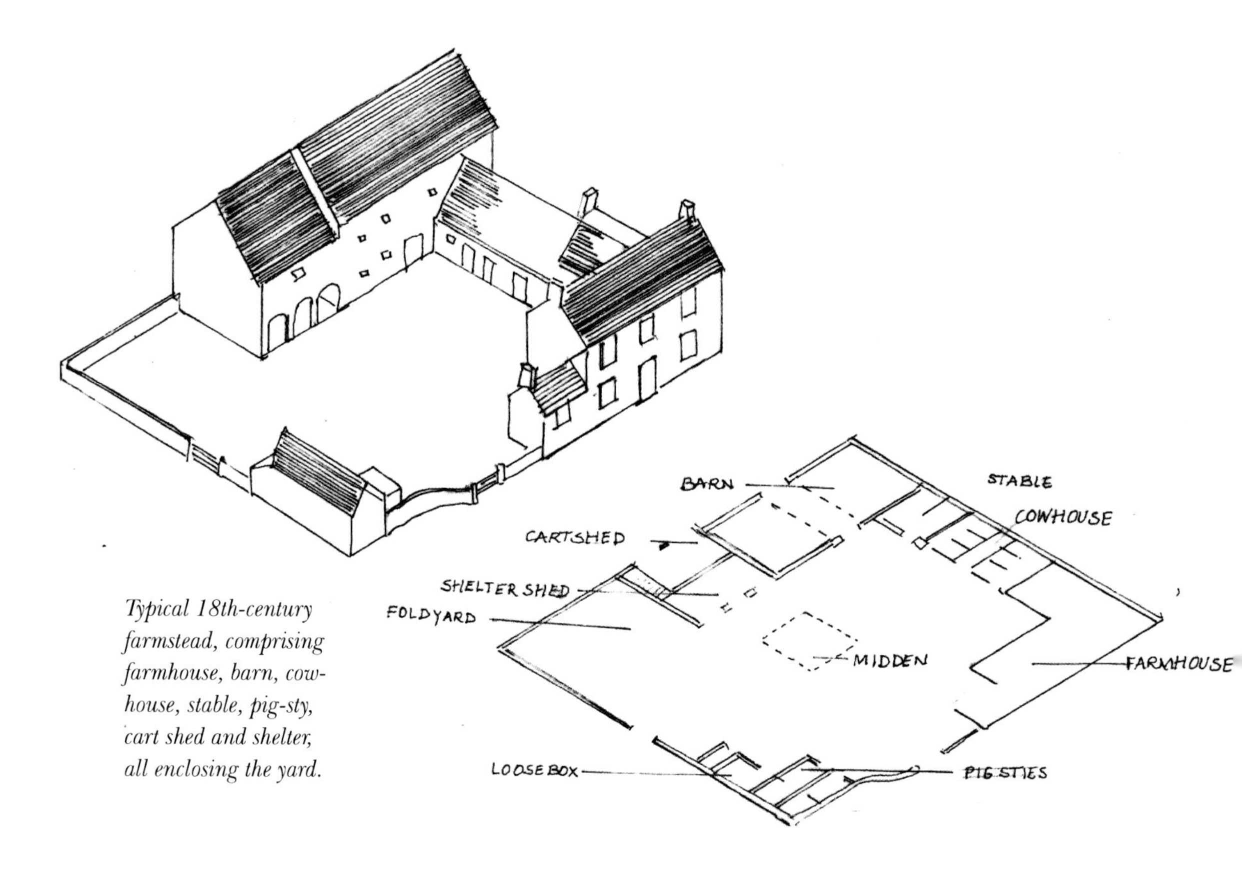

Typical 18th-century farmstead, comprising farmhouse, barn, cowhouse, stable, pig-sty, cart shed and shelter, all enclosing the yard.

community and provided a livelihood for many people. Today, just one per cent of the population manages the land that covers 90 per cent of the country, and many villages have become little more than commuter dormitories.

Modern farming's dependence on heavy machinery, monoculture planting and chemical sprays has largely destroyed the natural ecology of farmland and its value as a habitat for wildlife and native plants, and its soil has been compacted by machinery and impoverished by the loss of organic matter. Farm animals, reared in unnatural conditions, live miserable lives. Farm produce is contaminated by chemicals and lacks the nutrients and vitality necessary to sustain a healthy human population. Intensively reared livestock can actively threaten our health by introducing diseases into the food chain. Air and water are also contaminated by agrochemicals.

Healthy agriculture is the foundation of a civilisation; cultures that farm their environments to destruction do not survive. As the problems of industrial farming deepen and the rural environment continues to deteriorate, many people are seeking an alternative way of farming which works in harmony with nature. This new, ecological approach aims to re-establish the symbiotic relationship between people and their environment, while conserving natural resources, creating and sustaining a beautiful landscape, and respecting the rights of animals.

Eco-farming draws on elements of permacultural, biodynamic and organic systems with the aim of developing ways of using the land which are sustainable and which serve people much more effectively. Permaculture design is based on three land use ethics, which – with careful planning – are entirely compatible: care of the earth and all its life forms, care of people, and care of economic systems.

Eco-farms and eco-smallholdings can restore our landscape and rebuild its value to wildlife, by working with, rather than in opposition to, the natural ecology. They can help to restore the

Old farm buildings can be restored for homes and shelter, thereby restoring and enhancing the built landscape.

social fabric of our rural communities by generating local work, both on the land and in associated small businesses. They can produce the nutritious, organic, seasonal and local food needed to maintain a healthy human population and restore sustainability to our food chain. And they can do all this while being economically viable. Although labour costs may be higher on an ecological holding, the high prices of energy, fertilisers, pesticides and high-protein animal feeds are avoided, and if produce is sold locally, transport costs are kept to a minimum. As we pass the point of 'peak oil' and fossil fuels begin to run out, prices of inorganic inputs will rise steeply – so seeking out more sustainable alternatives will make increasing economic sense.

Ecological small farms and smallholdings are the way forward; they are the clear alternative, and the natural successors, to industrial farming, offering the opportunity to work the land in a holistic and sustainable way. Their role will become ever more important in the years ahead.

The key, however, is planning. A functional, attractive home farm landscape which works in harmony with nature does not come about by happy accident – it is the result of a carefully planned landscape design. Planning is necessary to any successful enterprise, and it is especially important where you are setting out with what, at first sight, seem to be contradictory goals. Unless money is no object, there is no point in making plans for your holding that are ecologically sound unless they are also practical and realistic.

Whether you are moving into an existing smallholding, creating an entirely new one or redeveloping your present smallholding, creating a management plan at the outset will allow you to achieve a successful enterprise that is also sustainable. It is entirely possible to create a beautiful, biodiverse landscape while at the same time developing an efficient, economically viable smallholding. If you plan and design carefully, you will be able to realise all your dreams for your property.

THE BENEFITS OF ECO-SMALLHOLDING

Eco-smallholding

- *realises the full potential of the land, while respecting it as a holistic, ecological resource*
- *ensures proper concern for nature, animals and people*
- *ensures a self-sufficient, self-reliant, sustainable farming system*
- *establishes a productive system modelled on an ecological landscape*
- *conserves all natural resources, including soil, water, trees, plants and wildlife*
- *recycles all waste on site, saves water and makes its own energy*
- *provides opportunities for employment and harmonious living on the land*
- *cares for all domestic animals in a natural and compassionate way*
- *produces a wide range of organic vegetables, fruit, nuts, herbs, fish, fowl and meat in harmony with nature*
- *provides the owners, and potentially the local community, with fresh, organic, seasonal foods*

1 THE PRINCIPLES OF ECO-FARMING

Sustainability

Sustainable land use starts with the understanding that you are merely the steward of your piece of land, not its owner in any absolute sense, and that your decisions need to leave it in good shape for future stewards to enjoy. Sustainable development has been defined as 'development which meets the needs of the present without compromising the ability of future generations to meet their own needs' (World Commission on Environment and Development, 1987).

Sustainability is a theme which needs to underpin the whole of the plans for a site; it cannot be regarded as an optional add-on, or treated as merely one section of the plan. When planning for sustainability, you need to consider your site as a whole, and to think about it in its wider context. If an enterprise is to be sustainable, you need to ensure that what you are doing in one area does not have a negative environmental impact elsewhere – either in another area of your own site, or beyond its boundaries. You cannot call a smallholding sustainable if, for instance, it uses peat products, the extraction of which cause irreversible damage to natural landscapes.

Ecological design

The first principle of ecological landscape design is that it should grow out of the landscape. How you design your site, and the ways in which you use it, need to chime with its natural ecology – its climate, water, soil, landform, aspect, flora and fauna. While you can sometimes adjust these factors in your favour, you cannot fundamentally alter them, and trying to impose unsuitable plans on a landscape is unsustainable and ecologically damaging. The more one designs in harmony with nature, the more effective and sustainable the system will become.

The second principle of ecological design is a recognition of the uniqueness of each site and of the people who live there. One imagines design to be an active process, but good ecological design is reactive. It is about looking at the landscape, listening to the people living there, and responding with tailor-made solutions. There is therefore no such thing as a model eco-smallholding, and the illustrations in this and similar publications are merely examples of what is possible.

The third important thing about good ecological design is that it is not finite; there is no point at which the design can be said to be complete. An ecological design is a living system in which people and the landscape interact. The ecosystem develops, plants grow and are harvested, animals live and die, and people's needs change. A good design will have the flexibility to evolve accordingly.

All animals need ample space – but different landscapes are more suited to different species, so this should be a major factor in your decision-making.

Organic methods are essential for the growing of crops on a sustainable smallholding.

Organic methods

An eco-smallholding is, by definition, organic. In terms of practical management, this means that your soil and crops will be free from chemicals, and that your animals will be fed naturally and reared compassionately. In terms of philosophy, it means working with nature, not in opposition to it. Instead of ignoring or destroying the life-enhancing characteristics of the natural ecosystem, as conventional agriculture does, an eco-smallholding is managed to conserve and utilise them.

On an eco-smallholding, the land can be fed with manures and compost, and through the planting of cover crops, and it can be replenished by the use of crop rotation. Nitrogen levels can be increased by using nitrogen-fixing leguminous plants, and pastures can be enriched by the inclusion of deep-rooting plants which retrieve minerals from the subsoil. Herbal ley seed mixtures can produce good grazing without the need for chemicals. The recycling of nutrients, trace elements and minerals can be facilitated by returning all organic wastes to the soil. This will reduce, and can eliminate, the need to import animal feed and soil fertilisers from outside the site.

Diversification

A key feature of an ecological system is its diversification. It is because natural ecosystems are diversified that they are robust and self-sustaining, and a sustainable smallholding should include a range of environments supporting different species of domestic animals and/or crop plants. Examples include gardens, woodlands, orchards, arable fields, grassland for grazing, and ponds for aquaculture. Monoculture, as practised on most modern farms, is bad for wildlife and the environment, requires high inputs of imported feed or fertiliser, and is a high-risk strategy; if something goes wrong, you can lose everything. Diversified systems are more stable as well as more sustainable.

A diversified eco-smallholding will also provide niches for a wide range of wildlife. While you cannot control what happens in the wider landscape, you can ensure that provision is made on your land for a range of wildlife habitats such as ponds, wild flower meadows, hedges and copses.

Eco-friendly options

Ecological design encompasses environmentally friendly choices such as buildings using natural materials, waste water treatment through reed beds, rainwater harvesting from roofs, porous paving, renewable energy systems and bioengineering. Modern farming consumes far more energy than it produces, but an eco-smallholding can produce its own energy from the sun, wind, water or biomass. Plants can supply biofuel, and animals biogas. You can even dispense with one need for fuel altogether if you use horses for ploughing! Rainwater can be harvested and stored, and waste water can be treated and reused.

Aesthetics

Agriculture has had hugely detrimental effects on the appearance of our landscape, with the erection of large, ugly, badly sited farm buildings, the loss of trees, hedgerows and watercourses, and the creation of vast, prairie-like fields. On an eco-smallholding, you can plan to retain or recreate a varied landscape, with hedgerows, woodlands and wild areas. These will yield their own harvest of nuts and berries and contribute to diversity and sustainability, as well as adding beauty to the landscape and giving pleasure to the people who work in it and visit it. Farm buildings can be designed to be attractive, or screened from view; they can be sited sympathetically, and they can be built from local and natural materials which will blend into the landscape.

If you are making changes to the appearance of your site, you need to consider how this will affect the surrounding landscape. Think not only about the individual features of your design, but about how these elements combine to make up the whole scene. If you live in a relatively unspoilt area, your aim should be to develop your site in a way that harmonises with the surrounding landscape. If, of course, you are surrounded by soulless farmland or urban sprawl, your aim will probably be different: to develop your land as an oasis where wildlife and people can find sanctuary.

The creation of an eco-smallholding offers the opportunity to restore interest and diversity to a soulless agricultural landscape.

2 ESSENTIAL ELEMENTS

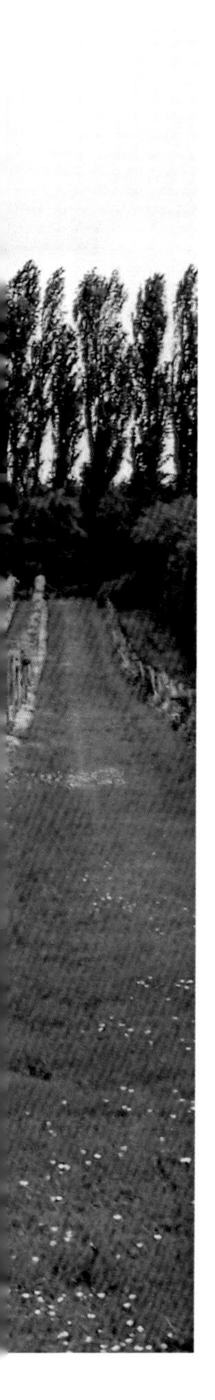

Scale and size

Many people imagine that to be a smallholder you need a substantial country property, and that because this is not an option for them, smallholding is a dream that needs to be endlessly deferred. In fact there are niches for smallholdings in the outskirts of towns and cities as well as in rural areas, and smallholding can be undertaken on a whole range of scales, from a large garden up to a small farm.

Large garden holding
(up to 0.5 hectares/1.25 acres)

With a large garden, it is entirely possible to set yourself up as a smallholder, though the range and number of activities you can pursue will be limited. Growing fruit and vegetables will probably be your major activity. Keeping livestock is likely to be constrained by lack of space, and possibly by the proximity of neighbours, but the smaller types of poultry or a couple of beehives might be an option.

On this scale you will be producing food largely for your own consumption, with the possibility of some surpluses to sell at peak times of year. You could consider a small-scale enterprise like making jams and chutneys to add value to your produce. A smallholding of this size can be managed by one person on a hobby basis, in addition to a full-time job, though you will be working long hours at busy times of year.

Small holding (0.5-1.5 hectares/1.25-3.5 acres)

If you have a small holding, you can consider more types of livestock – a small flock of sheep or goats, a few pigs, the bigger types of poultry – and you would also have space to grow some fodder crops. You could be producing considerable surpluses of fruit and/or vegetables to sell, and an 'added value' enterprise could be undertaken on a bigger scale. A holding of this size would probably be too much for one person in a full-time job, but could be managed around part-time work, or between a couple.

Medium holding (1.5-4 hectares/3.5-10 acres)

If you have a medium-sized holding, you can aspire to be self-sufficient in all of the foods you are producing, as well as having large surpluses to sell or process for sale. You can keep several types of livestock, and larger species, notably cattle, become a possibility. You can also grow crops on a field scale. You should be careful, however, not to diversify too far and spread yourself too thin. Farming on this scale is a full-time job for at least one person, and it is no longer possible to do everything by hand; you will need to buy, or hire, machinery, or draft in extra labour at busy times of year.

Large holding (4-8 hectares/10-20 acres)

On a large holding, you can keep larger numbers of the bigger species of livestock, and you will certainly be working on a field scale. You will have space for a proper farmyard with a range of buildings for animals, storage and work activities. On this scale, smallholding is a full-time activity for at least two people; you will certainly need machinery, and you may also need extra help at peak times of year. You will certainly be selling produce and making an income from your farm, and could consider a full-scale 'on-farm' enterprise like cheese-making.

Design elements

Livestock

For a smallholder, unlike a farmer, the decision about what animals to keep is rarely a commercial one; it has much more to do with which species you have an affinity with. However, the decision should not be made on sentimental grounds alone. You need to assess the suitability of your land and climate for the species you have in mind, think carefully about the work and cost of keeping them, and be sure that you have the facilities, skills and time to give them the care they need.

Chickens, like all animals, need to be allowed to range freely – but they also need to be protected from predators.

Kitchen garden crops

The kitchen garden may take up just part of your land, or it may be your entire smallholding. On a larger site, you may have space for a separate orchard and a designated herb garden as well as a vegetable plot. If space is limited, herbs and short-term fruit crops can share space with your vegetables, while perennial fruit could be grown in your ornamental garden, or against south-facing walls.

If you only have a small area, careful crop planning will be necessary to get the best possible return on your growing area, and to ensure that you are also able to rotate your annual vegetable crops, and rest and replenish the land. If you have a large holding and want to undertake a range of additional activities, it is vital that you plan the kitchen garden so that it runs with the minimum of effort.

If you have a choice of sites for your vegetable garden, opt for the best possible soil, a south- or west-facing aspect, and an open site. Avoid overhanging trees or nearby hedges, or plan to remove them, and site the plot clear of the dense shade cast by buildings. Avoid frost pockets; the ideal site has a gentle slope, so that frost rolls across it and away. Too steep a slope, however, will create problems with soil erosion, and a very steep garden is difficult to cultivate.

If the site needs to be cleared of pernicious weeds, allow a year for doing that before expecting to get crops from the land. If rabbits are a problem, plan to install heavy-duty fencing as your first priority. You will also need a greenhouse or polytunnel, a shed, a compost area, and water butts and/or convenient access to mains water.

Field and fodder crops

On a field scale, you need to grow the crops that will do well in your soil and climate; you cannot provide shelter, or significantly amend the soil, on this scale. Bear in mind, however, that if your neighbours are farming on a commercial basis, the profitability of particular crops will have been a major factor in their decisions. Commercial considerations are probably not your first priority, and it may make more sense to concentrate on the crops that you need to feed your animals through the winter.

The house is usually the hub of a smallholding, with functional buildings clustered around it.

The farmstead

If you have a big enough holding, you will have, or can create, a proper farmyard. The buildings it needs to contain will depend on the enterprises you have in mind; they could include barns, sheds and holding areas for livestock, storage sheds for crops, tools and machinery, workshops, and buildings for enterprises such as dairying.

The farmyard should be easily accessible from the house, since as a smallholder you are permanently on call. However, it is also important that the farmyard does not intrude on the home. If possible, it is good to plan for a separate driveway and

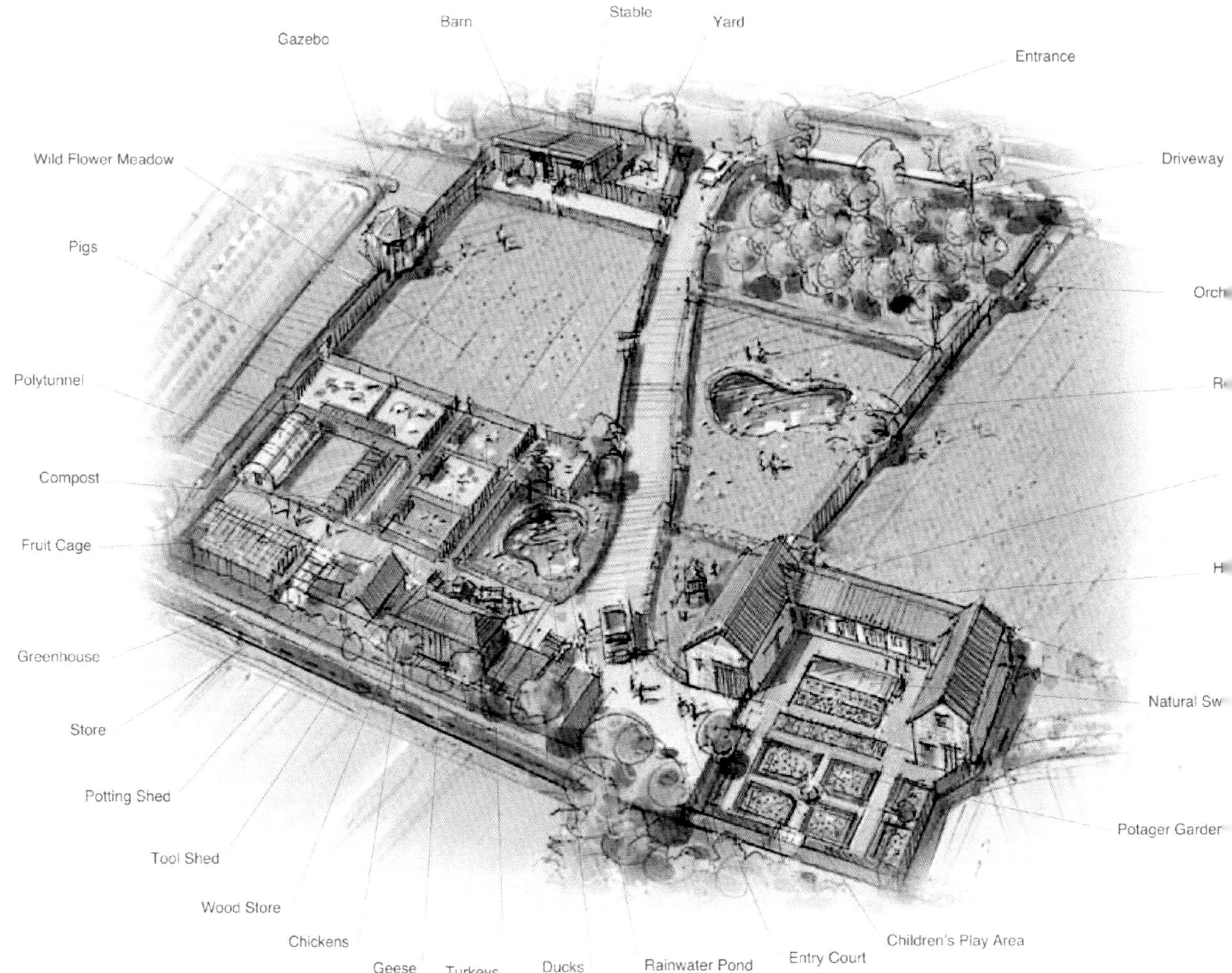

THE FARMSTEAD

The farmstead is the heart of a smallholding.

entrance court for the house, so that the dirt of the farmstead can be kept there.

If your smallholding is on a smaller scale, you will still need a range of buildings or structures, such as a chicken shed, a workshop, a compost area, or a frost-free building in which to store crops. Siting these correctly is essential to the efficient functioning of the holding. For instance, the chicken shed needs to be near the house, so that shutting it at dusk is less of a chore, and the compost area should be conveniently near the vegetable plot.

Alternative technology

A key part of a sustainable lifestyle is a move towards greater self-sufficiency in energy, water and resources. As climate change escalates, this can no longer be considered an optional add-on; it should be regarded as an essential. Utilising alternative technology on a domestic scale is becoming increasingly practical and affordable; there is much more choice within the various systems, and the costs have all become much more reasonable. In addition, the government's Feed-In Tariff and Renewable Heat Incentive schemes make payments for energy generated and fed back into the grid, and these help to offset the capital outlay.

How self-sufficient you wish to be, and in what areas, depends on your circumstances and aspirations. For some, it is enough to collect rainwater for garden use, for instance, while others want to recycle enough water to become entirely independent of the mains. A key question, when considering alternative energy sources, is whether you wish to retain a connection to mains services as a back-up and in order to earn tariffs, or to opt for complete independence.

It is important to factor your house into your energy-saving plans. An ecological way of life starts at home, and it makes little sense to farm in a sustainable way while living in an energy-inefficient house full of resource-hungry appliances. Alongside renewable energy options, it is important to consider the other side of the coin and plan for insulation, double- or triple-glazing and energy-efficient appliances.

Renewable energy

There are four major ways in which energy can be obtained renewably and – after the initial outlay on equipment – for free: from the sun, from wind, from water and from biomass (vegetation). Which to choose depends on a number of factors: the location and size of your property, the availability of the necessary energy source (sunshine, wind, running water, or land and a suitable climate for growing trees), the capital outlay you are prepared for, the payback period you require, and which of them appeals to you.

Economies of scale mean that co-operative ventures, involving more than one household or even an entire community, may be a more financially viable option, so your decision may also be affected by what is already in place, or planned, in your local area.

Solar power

Solar energy can be used to heat water and generate electricity, if you have a suitable south-facing sloping roof on which to site the solar panels. On average, domestic systems will provide approximately 50 per cent of the energy required to deliver hot water, allowing for heat losses from stored water. They are used in conjunction with another heat source such as a wood burner, which can bring warm water up to the required temperature using very little additional energy. Photovoltaic cells can convert solar energy into electrical energy, which can then be converted to 240v AC by means of an inverter, which can be located in an outbuilding. Photovoltaic cell panels can operate even in cloudy conditions in the UK, and will last for 20 to 30 years.

Wind power

Wind has been used to generate power for centuries in this country, as can be seen by the very old windmills still in existence. If local wind speeds are sufficient over the course of the year, this can be an effective way of generating your electricity. Modern wind turbines are suitable for domestic use as they are very slim and only around 3m (10ft) tall, so they do not cause an adverse impact on the landscape if they are sited correctly. As with solar panels, an inverter will be necessary to convert the electricity generated to the 240v system.

Hydro-electric power

Water wheels were once widely used across the country, and if you have a stream on your property this can be harnessed as a reliable means of generating electricity using a micro-hydro generator. These have improved considerably in recent years and can operate constantly, even if the flow rate of the stream is reduced during the summer months. The power output is directly proportional to the flow rate, but conveniently, summer is the time when energy demand is at its lowest.

Biomass

If you have sufficient land and a suitable climate for growing trees, wood is an ideal fuel for heating and cooking. Hedges can also be managed to produce some wood for fuel. A suitable storage area will be required so that the timber is kept dry until it is well seasoned. Depending on the type of wood and the location of the store, it can take up to three years before it is ready for burning.

Rainwater harvesting

The aim of rainwater harvesting is to collect water from the roofs of buildings and store it in suitable containers for use for garden watering and outdoor cleaning applications. With the right systems in place it can also be used for toilet flushing and washing machines. The containers can range from water butts to underground storage tanks, depending on the scale of your aspirations and the initial cost you are prepared for. Filtration will be necessary to prevent leaves and other debris from

entering the container or tank via the gutter and downpipe system. Water can also be stored in a pond, and this option has additional aesthetic and wildlife benefits.

Waste water treatment

'Grey' water – household waste water from baths, showers and laundry – can be reused for outdoor applications. Replumbing is required to separate out the grey water from 'black' water – kitchen sink, dishwasher and toilet waste – after which it can be filtered and used for watering non-edible crops, or for cleaning purposes. A refinement of the system is to direct the water into a garden wetland – a shallow pond filled with gravel and soil and planted with specialised water-cleaning plants. This will purify the water in the same way that a natural wetland does, after which it can be channelled into a pond or stored in a tank for extended periods.

If space permits, a separate reed bed would also allow you to clean your black waste water. A reed bed is a pond into which liquid effluent is channelled, the solids having been removed. It is generally lined to prevent any seepage into adjacent ground and filled with gravel and soil, which acts as a base for the reeds and aquatic plants. The waste water is converted by the plants, their attendant microbes and the chemical properties of the soil into clear, clean water. Reed beds can work in conjunction with a septic tank system, or independently. Proper design and maintenance is, of course, essential.

Natural building

Buildings such as barns, workshops, studios and sheds can be built from natural materials such as timber, stone, recycled bricks, tiles and second-hand items such as doors and windows.

With careful design and locally appropriate choices, such buildings can be aesthetically pleasing and will blend into the landscape far more readily than those made from synthetic materials.

Bioengineering

'Bioengineering' refers to elements in the built landscape, such as retaining walls, paved surfaces and building roofs, which use plants in their construction. This not only improves their appearance by making them less harsh and overpowering but also allows for better drainage and overall functioning. For example, retaining walls can use a timber crib method of construction that has plants growing in the spaces. For paving, a similar crib system made from concrete can be used; this is generally known as 'grasscrete', as grass is grown in the spaces. Roofs of buildings can be made into gardens, using lightweight materials for both surfaces and plant containers, or planted up as 'green' roofs. Bioengineering methods can also be used for the stabilisation of sloping ground.

Wildlife conservation

The final essential element on a sustainable smallholding is conservation. An eco-smallholding offers the opportunity to conserve, restore and enhance the landscape by, for instance, planting woodland, replanting hedgerows, sowing meadows, adding bankside planting to streams, and deepening ponds. If such features can be linked, or they adjoin wild areas beyond the boundaries of your site, biological corridors can be created, which will allow species to migrate and recolonise other areas.

The areas with the greatest wildlife value are often ones which humans consider to be 'waste' ground, such as thickets and swamps. It is easy to be tempted to tidy these up in order to 'improve' the appearance of the landscape, but if you can accommodate them into your design, you will provide a habitat for a wide range of species. Forest edge is the zone of highest wildlife activity, so underplanting trees with native shrubs and herbaceous plants is of huge benefit.

Thoughtful landscape conservation will allow your site to become a habitat for a wide range of wildlife and native plants. With careful planning and management, it is entirely possible to advance conservation projects alongside a working – and profitable – smallholding. *See Appendix 3: Aids for wildlife conservation.*

'Bug banks' around field margins are both a haven for wildlife and a boon to the smallholder who works in harmony with nature.

ELEMENTS CHECKLIST

Buildings

- [ ] *SHEDS*

  Tools, equipment, machinery
- [ ] *STORAGE*

  Fertilisers, firewood
- [ ] *STABLES*
- [ ] *BARN*
- [ ] *SERVICES, PUMPS, ENGINES*

Structures

- [ ] *PROTECTED CROPS*

  Greenhouses, polytunnels, cold frames
- [ ] *COMPOST BINS*
- [ ] *ANIMAL PROTECTION UNITS*

Animals

- [ ] *SMALL*

  Poultry, rabbits, pigs, bees
- [ ] *LARGE*

  Goats, sheep, cattle, horses/ponies, other

Food production

- [ ] *PROTECTED*

  Vegetables, herbs
- [ ] *ORCHARDS*

  Fruit

Major land uses

- [ ] *FODDER CROPS*
- [ ] *GRASSLAND*
- [ ] *WETLAND*
- [ ] *WOODLAND*
- [ ] *HEDGES/HEDGEROWS*

Wildlife

- [ ] *HABITATS*

3 PLANNING FOR SUCCESS

The benefits of planning

A country property is probably the biggest investment you will ever make. No sooner are you settled in, however, than more expenditure looms. It is rare to find a property in perfect order, and you will have brought your own dreams and plans with you. To make those a reality, new buildings will need to be erected, new landscapes created, and new services installed, and existing ones will need to be repaired or modified. There are important decisions to be made: the alignment of a barn, the positioning of a polytunnel, the routing of a water supply.

The investment is not merely financial. A move to the land is generally a long-cherished dream. With this level of emotional investment, it is vital to do whatever you can to ensure that the reality lives up to your expectations. Success with smallholding depends on many things – determination, discipline, willingness to work hard, skill, experience and, at times, luck – but it also requires clear goals and sensible priorities. And in order to translate those into day to day management and year on year progress, you need to have a plan.

An overall management plan will ensure that you make the best use of your land practically, naturally and visually. Even small sites require meticulous planning to ensure that the land is used to best advantage throughout the year. If you are taking on a large holding, organising its management is a job in itself, and it is very difficult to manage it in a consistent and purposeful way without a plan. Whatever the size of your site, good planning is key to achieving the necessary balance between maintenance tasks, like day to day animal husbandry, and progress tasks, like building a new barn.

Where major building projects are concerned, proceeding without a plan can mean a great deal of wasted time, labour and expense. Hindsight is a valuable thing, but foresight is rather better where expensive building work is concerned. Whether you are starting out with a new property, or developing an existing one, starting with a plan will ensure that the decisions you make are the right ones.

Planning will also help to assess the financial viability of the operation. If you are intending to produce an income from your smallholding, proper planning is essential to ensure that this becomes a reality. If you are intending to apply for grants for things such as the upkeep of hedgerows and the planting of new woodland, planning will allow you to identify where payments are available and ensure that you know what you need to achieve, and by what deadlines, in order to claim them.

The process of producing a plan can be as important as the plan itself. It will let you clarify your aims and aspirations, and open your eyes to possibilities you may not have thought of. The planning process provides a vehicle for sharing ideas, resolving disagreements, achieving consensus and securing the involvement of the various people who have an interest in the site. If you have a family, they need to be involved in every stage of creating a plan, and anyone who will work on the smallholding should be consulted about all areas that might concern them. In this way, everyone involved will have an investment in the final plan, and be committed to its successful implementation.

When your management plan has been created, you will have a clear vision of how to proceed and a programme of work which will let you move towards defined and achievable goals. You will be confident that your construction projects are based

Regional location plan

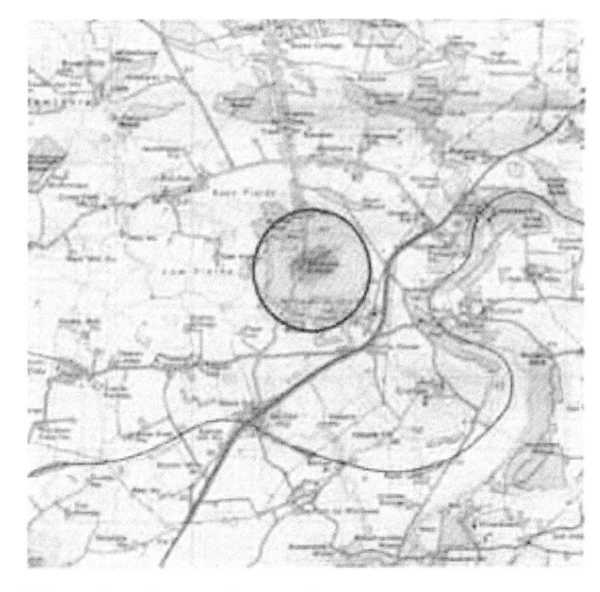

District location plan

Aerial photo

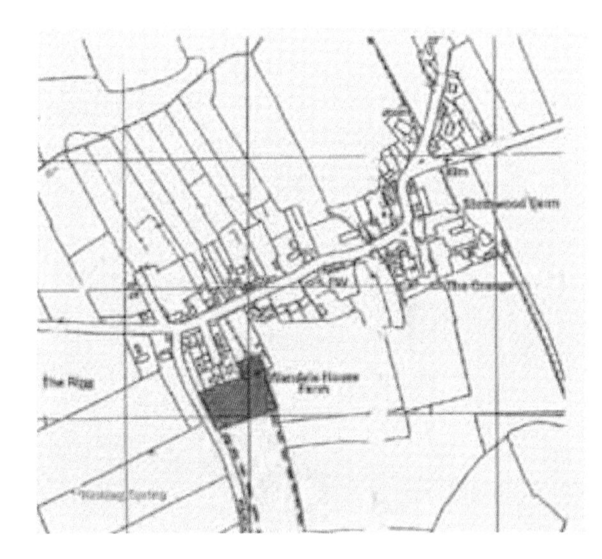

Local location plan

on sound decisions, thus avoiding the risk of costly mistakes. You will be clear that you are using your land in the best possible way, and confident that you will be able to realise your dreams in harmony with nature.

However, any plan must have a degree of flexibility built into it. For first-time smallholders, the biggest challenge is deciding what crops to grow and what livestock to keep, and this will inevitably involve some trial and error in the early stages. It is therefore important to allow yourself the flexibility to alter your plans as you learn from your experiences. A plan needs to be constantly revisited and reviewed, and should be regarded as a guide, not a prescription.

Who should produce your plan?

The key decision at this stage is whether to create your management plan yourself or employ a professional to do it. Doing it yourself has many benefits. You will be able to devote as much time as you wish to it, and take as long as you like, and it will not cost you anything. Particularly if you are already living there, you know your site best, and you have the best understanding of your aspirations and resources. You may well find it easier to translate all this into a plan of your own than to communicate it adequately to a third party. In addition, creating a plan yourself will give you a greater sense of ownership of it, which will increase the likelihood of you seeing it through into action.

On the other hand, you probably do not have the time, facilities or skills needed to do the job as well as it could be done. Surveying equipment, for instance, is needed to produce a detailed map of all but the smallest sites, and a professional will be able to assess your site and make accurate judgements about things that no amount of looking would make you aware of. A specialist will also approach your site objectively, whereas your assessments will inevitably be clouded by emotion and preconceived ideas.

If you employ a specialist, they will undertake or commission a proper survey, and supply you with professionally drawn plans of the final design. At the end of the process, you will have a professionally drawn-up report, containing maps, plans, designs and a costed work programme, which will serve as a focus for continued motivation and an inspirational record of the whole project.

Unless, having read this chapter, you are confident that you are equipped to do the job yourself, it makes sense to involve a professional in some or all of the planning process. It may seem expensive, but it should be regarded as an investment, since it will save money, time and effort in the long run. If you do decide to undertake most of the work yourself, a middle way would be to employ one or more specialists to help with particular tasks. On all but the smallest of sites, the survey is one job that should really be done by a professional. You may also wish to consult specialists about specific aspects of your plans – a building surveyor, a renewable energy advisor or an arboriculturist, for instance.

If you employ someone to undertake some or all of the work of planning and designing your smallholding, it is important, as with any job, that you ensure that they are competent and professionally qualified. You also need to specify exactly what you require, and you must ensure that the person has all the information you consider necessary to the decision-making process.

A management plan

A management plan is a document that assesses your site as it is today and sets out how best to reach your goals for the future. It includes detailed designs that show you the best location for new structures and features, based on a careful assessment of the various options. It also contains a costed programme of

BENEFITS OF A MANAGEMENT PLAN

A management plan will:

- *Help you to clarify your aims and aspirations for your property*
- *Identify possibilities for the site which you had not thought of*
- *Achieve consensus between family members with differing ideas for the property*
- *Identify the appropriate areas for the functions and elements in your design*
- *Show how all the features of the site can be utilised and developed sustainably*
- *Ensure the conservation and enhancement of the site's natural resources*
- *Ensure that visual and aesthetic elements are given proper consideration*
- *Set out a logical programme of work*
- *Allow work to be phased according to budget*
- *Identify future requirements and further possibilities for the site*
- *Provide a permanent record of the whole project*
- *Act as a focus for continued motivation*
- *Support any grant aid applications*

work that will let you proceed in the most efficient and economical way. A management plan is often a precondition for grant aid applications, and will certainly assist with any that you make in the future.

A management plan will consider all the elements in your landscape, from the built environment – the house, barns, sheds, roads, tracks and so on – to natural features such as ponds, woodlands and hedges. It will consider provision for animals, both livestock and wildlife, and food-growing requirements: the kitchen garden, orchard, greenhouses or polytunnels, and field crops. It will take account of all the uses of the property – practical, economic, aesthetic and recreational – and find ways to reconcile your plans for conservation with the practical and economic demands of a working smallholding.

Purpose

The main purpose of a management plan is to enable you to design and manage your site effectively. Exactly what that means will depend on your site, the people involved, and the plans you have. You should always be clear about why you are producing a management plan before you start, since this will affect what you include in it. It may be useful to start by writing down the specific purposes of your plan.

Another important decision at this stage is the timescale of your plan. You may want to create a plan covering two, five or ten years, depending on the length of time over which you envisage implementing your design.

Contents

Management plans vary greatly in length, structure and complexity, depending on the size of the site and the aims with which they are produced. There is no single correct format for a plan, nor a single formula for producing one; the contents and structure of a plan are flexible and should reflect your needs and the demands of your site. However, all plans contain some basic elements.

Most plans begin with an introduction which states the purposes of the plan. In all but the shortest of plans, a contents list is helpful. All plans should then include an assessment of the site. Longer plans will present this as a comprehensive site description, followed by a separate evaluation section. The plan will then set out proposals for the development of the site. These may include an overall vision for the site and its design, followed by a statement of management objectives and the methods by which these will be achieved.

The plan may then contain a work programme which breaks down the proposals for the site into individual tasks or projects. It may also identify the necessary financial, human and material resources to see the projects through. It is sometimes appropriate to present these as a separate financial plan, especially if you are seeking outside funding.

It is important that the plan includes provision for monitoring and review, which means revisiting the plan periodically and checking on how successfully it is being implemented. The plan may conclude with appendices, which are useful for presenting supplementary information like species lists or historical data.

Assessment

The first step in creating a management plan is to assess what already exists. There are two sides to this: people and property. You need to ascertain your own aims and requirements, and then undertake a thorough evaluation of the existing site.

AIMS AND REQUIREMENTS

The first stage is to clarify your aims: the purpose of creating the plan and the key principles which will underlie the management of the site. You then need to ascertain what you

THE PROCESS

AIMS

A broad statement of the principles which will underlie the management of the land.

SURVEY

A comprehensive record of what exists on the land and its present management.

REQUIREMENTS

A summary of the owners' requirements and their aspirations for the property.

ANALYSIS

An interpretation of all the survey information, identifying the inter-relationship between existing and potential land uses. Problems, conflicts and opportunities examined. From the decisions reached, the Objectives are then formulated.

OBJECTIVES

Specific statements on how the Aims are to be realised in both the shorter and longer terms for all the various land uses.

DESIGN

Drawings produced to show the proposed layout for the various uses of the land covering the whole property.

OVERVIEW

A summary of the work required and the resources needed to achieve the Objectives and the Design, and their approximate costs.

IMPLEMENTATION

A detailed action programme drawn up from the Overview that will allow the implementation of the work according to the agreed budget and time.

MONITORING & REVIEW

A record and assessment of management achievements together with proposals for periodic review.

want from your property, and what you can bring to it: your aspirations, requirements and resources. This part of the process is covered in detail in Chapter 4.

SURVEY

The next step is to assess the existing site, and then to present your findings in the form of a detailed topographic survey, alongside whatever additional maps and plans prove to be necessary or helpful, and a site description, which will record all the findings about the site that cannot be conveyed in visual form. Chapter 5 explains the entire survey process.

Analysis

The next stage is the analysis, which interprets the information provided by the survey drawings and the site description, in the light of your aims and requirements.

Preliminary sketches, drawings and estimates can now be drawn up, to explore different solutions to problems and possible layouts for the design. These can then form a basis for discussions, until agreement is reached on the best way forward. The analysis stage is covered in Chapter 6.

Design concepts and final design

One or more design concepts can now be produced, on the basis of all the information gathered. Once the design has been agreed, a final design drawing is produced. The design process is the subject of Chapter 7.

Implementation

The final stage is to draw up a detailed programme of work covering labour, materials, time and costs, and to make provision for monitoring and review. The process of implementation is covered in Chapter 8.

MANAGEMENT PLAN CHECKLIST

- [ ] *The purposes of the plan*
- [ ] *The timescale of the plan*
- [ ] *Who will produce the plan*
- [ ] *Identify the key stages in producing the plan*
- [ ] *Identify individuals who need to be consulted about the plan*
- [ ] *Decide how the plan is going to be produced, and in what format*
- [ ] *Identify all sources of information about the site*
- [ ] *Ascertain your aims and aspirations for the site*
- [ ] *Undertake a site survey*
- [ ] *Compile a site description*
- [ ] *Check all existing designations and legal aspects of the site*
- [ ] *Assemble an archive of information about the site*
- [ ] *Carry out a site evaluation*
- [ ] *Identify all the important features of the site*
- [ ] *Consider the site's context and surroundings*
- [ ] *Express your vision for the site*
- [ ] *Decide on your management objectives*
- [ ] *Decide on a final design for the site*
- [ ] *Break down your objectives into a work programme*
- [ ] *Identify responsibility for each project, and the resources required*
- [ ] *Decide how you will monitor the progress of your plan*

4 AIMS AND REQUIREMENTS

Aspirations

Planning and designing start with assessment: in order to plan for the future, you first need to know what exists today. The first thing is to assess what you want from your land. What are your aims, aspirations and needs? The next question is what you have to offer: what skills, resources, time and money can you bring to the project?

Then you need to assess your property – or the property you want. Ideally, the planning process should start before you purchase a piece of land, so that you are sure that you are buying the best site for your aspirations and needs. Once you have secured the right property, you need to assess exactly what you have. Only then can you begin to consider the changes you want to make.

It is essential to remember that this stage of the process is about looking and listening, which are reactive processes, not active ones. You need to avoid the temptation to start making value judgements or decisions at this stage. This can be difficult, because you will already have ideas for your property, and further ideas will present themselves as you assess the site. If you let these assume the status of decisions at this early stage, you will close off other possibilities.

Instead, you should add any new ideas to your wish list, and stay firmly in listening mode. Only once the assessment is complete should you shift into the active designing mode. At the evaluation stage you will start to make judgements about what you have learned from the assessment, and at the design stage you will translate those judgements into decisions about the best way to proceed.

Wants and needs

If you were designing a site for someone else, you would obviously sit down with them and compile a list of what they wanted. You need to do this just as systematically when you are designing for yourself. It helps to compile a list of questions and then work through it methodically, so you can be sure that you have covered everything. This can also provide a chance for less assertive members of the family or group to have their say.

List the practical things you need and want: the animals you want to keep and the facilities you will need for them, the crops you want to grow and the areas of land they will require. Note your other aspirations, such as growing wood for fuel, recycling household water, or generating renewable energy. If you want to be self-sufficient in any area, or to produce a surplus to sell, you will need to work out the quantities required and the space and facilities that will be necessary.

Also list the other things you want from the site. This will include your plans for conservation and wildlife habitats: hedges, ponds, copses, wild areas and so on. It will also include amenities for yourself and your family: facilities for recreation, leisure and play, and abstract qualities like space, beauty and privacy.

If you have an overall ambition for your piece of land, record this, but make sure that you also record all your secondary aspirations. It is easy for these to be lost in the midst of a grand scheme, and you may also find that your priorities shift as you start to evaluate the practicalities. Your long-held dream may not, in fact, be the best option once everything has been considered.

If you have already found a site, think about what you like and dislike about it. What aspects do you want to keep as they are, and what do you want to remove? What changes would you like to make? If you are already living on the site, think about what things work best, what works less well, and what might work better if it were moved or changed.

You will almost certainly find that not everything on your wish list is compatible, particularly if you are canvassing opinion from several people. At this stage, just note everything that is asked for, without attempting to reconcile competing demands. That is a task for the evaluation stage of the process. It is, however, worth assigning priority to items on the list; if you regard some things as essential and others as optional extras, that should be noted.

Visioning

Next, let your imagination run free. Visioning is a brainstorming process, where you allow yourself to come up with ideas without allowing practical considerations to get in the way.

Ask yourself a series of 'open' questions. What do you want and need from the landscape? What can it offer you? What will

A new site offers the opportunity to create the smallholding you want – but you need to work with the existing landscape.

you do there? What does the landscape, and the surrounding area, need? Does it need to be restored, or improved? How should the new landscape look and feel? Do you have an overriding vision for the site – a wildlife sanctuary, a demonstration garden, an educational resource, or simply the perfect place for you to live and work?

Personal resources

What you want from your smallholding is only half the story; the other side of the coin is what you can bring to it. If you were creating a management plan for other people, you would need to ask carefully worded questions to find out what personal and financial resources they had: their available time, energy, skills and budget. When assessing your own resources, it is vital that you do so honestly and realistically.

Time

Be aware that when you are planning and designing your smallholding, you are probably at the peak of your enthusiasm. Do not, therefore, overestimate the amount of time and energy you will be able or willing to devote to implementing the design or – crucially – to maintaining it. Remember also that practical work always takes longer than the time you allow for it!

Think about how the time demands of your plans will mesh with your other commitments and priorities. Livestock requires you to be available at set times each day, all year round, while growing vegetables will demand extra hours through the growing season. However, you may be able to source extra labour for free at busy times of year; the lure of an eco-smallholding is such that friends and family may jump at the chance of a working holiday at lambing or harvesting time.

Remember that you need to allow time both for

implementing new elements of your design and for maintaining your existing smallholding activities. Achieving a balance between 'progress' and 'maintenance' tasks can be challenging. It is often better to implement a design over several years, rather than trying to put everything in place at once; this staggers the 'progress' work, and allows the new maintenance tasks it generates to be absorbed into your daily workload a little at a time.

Energy

Be realistic about your energy levels, your health and fitness, and the limitations posed by any disability you have. You need to be sure that these are compatible with your aspirations. If you are starting out in smallholding later in life, you may want to create plans for your holding which allow you to gradually wind things down as you get older.

Skills

Think carefully about the skills you will need to achieve what you want to do, whether that is embarking on an activity like cheesemaking, or undertaking a landscaping project like laying hedgerows. Be realistic about your abilities, and if you do not have the necessary skills, acquire them, by attending courses or apprenticing yourself to someone experienced, before setting out on your own. Learning from your mistakes can be costly and time-consuming and, where animals are concerned, it is unkind.

If you are new to gardening or farming, it makes sense to start out with crops and animals that do not need any special skills or knowledge. Garden vegetables and chickens are an easier way into smallholding than field crops and cattle, and it is far better to start small and expand gradually than to take on too much too soon.

If a specific skill is required in the set-up stages – to erect a polytunnel, for instance, or indeed to create a management plan

– it may be easier to buy in the help of an expert. Another option is to draft in help from friends and neighbours with skills and experience; if you build and maintain your support networks, smallholding is not something you have to undertake single-handed.

Budget

Budget is of course a key consideration. As well as how much money you have at your disposal, it is also important to note the pattern of when it will be available; you may have a lump sum to invest in the project, or you may be able to spend a regular smaller amount from your income. If you have grant funding, this may need to be spent by a certain date, or in several specified instalments. These considerations will affect the nature of your design, and the timescale over which it is implemented.

A major financial question is whether you intend your smallholding to be profit-making, self-financing or subsidised. You may want to make an income from your smallholding, in which case your plan will include producing surpluses to sell. You may be aiming to sell enough to make a profit, so that your smallholding covers some or all of your living expenses, or just to earn enough to cover the costs of other activities on your land, like conservation projects. Alternatively, you may be happy to treat smallholding as a hobby which you subsidise with income from other employment or savings. Which of these financial models applies to you will obviously be a major factor in your plans.

Smallholding selection

If you have yet to find your smallholding, the assessment of your aspirations and resources should ideally be done before you start looking. Making a list is always a good idea when you go shopping, and never more so than when you are buying your dream property. It is easy to fall in love with a place, but you need to think practically as well as emotionally to be sure that the reality will live up to your dreams. New possibilities open up once you actually start viewing properties, so you do need to build a degree of flexibility into your plans. That does not, however, mean giving in to the temptation of abandoning sensible plans and priorities just because you have seen the 'perfect' property under brilliant blue skies.

Needs and wants

If you are clear about what you need and want from your smallholding, and have done the necessary research in advance, you will know the right questions to ask when you view potential properties. If you plan to keep livestock, you will need to enquire about the quality of grazing, the suitability of the land for fodder crops, and the siting and condition of barns and sheds. If you want to grow vegetables, your questions will be about soil type, shelter, climate, aspect and water, and about the provision and condition of greenhouses and/or polytunnels. If you want to generate wind or solar power, you will need to find out about wind speed, or the alignment of roofs.

There are four basic factors to consider when assessing the potential uses of a piece of land: climate, water, soil and topography. The interaction of these determines what is possible in a given locality, and none of them can be changed to any real extent. There is no point in trying to impose preconceived ideas on a piece of land; you need to work with the conditions you have – so the moral is to make sure that you get ones you can work with.

Key climatic factors are the highest and lowest likely temperatures, the likelihood of snow and frost, the annual rainfall and the prevailing wind. If spring is late, this may prevent early sowing, or early lambing. If rainfall is high, it may be difficult to work the soil in spring and autumn. If it is low, you may not be able to produce good grass for grazing, or abundant vegetable crops. If flooding is a potential problem, that can spell disaster for any sort of enterprise.

Soil and geology are crucial considerations if you are planning to grow crops. The key issue is the quality and depth of the topsoil; other factors are soil pH (how acid or alkaline it is) and the levels of the major soil nutrients. A very acid or alkaline soil, or one which is significantly impoverished, is difficult to amend sufficiently to make successful growing possible. You also need to determine whether the soil is predominantly clay, sand, silt or loam; this will determine its water-holding capacity, and has implications for its fertility and how easy it is to work.

Think about how the topography of a site will affect your plans. Very steep land is unsuitable for most farming activities, sloping land is more difficult to manage and access, and very flat land may be barren and unsheltered. The orientation of slopes is also an important factor; a south- or southwest-facing site is ideal, while a north- or north-easterly situation will be challenging, particularly for growing fruit and vegetables. The height of the site above sea level will have implications for temperature, the length of the season, and the likelihood of frosts. The level of the water table will determine how well the land drains, and is a factor in whether it is prone to flooding.

You are unlikely to be lucky enough to find the perfect smallholding in 'move-into' condition, so it will probably be a question of deciding whether a property can be upgraded into what you want, given your available resources. You can adapt, alter or add to an existing property, but while some things can easily be changed, others will be expensive or difficult to change, and some cannot be changed. Do some careful thinking, planning and costing before you decide to go ahead with the purchase of a less than ideal property. If your budget is very limited, you may need to wait until a property comes up where much of the necessary work for your purposes has already been done.

ASSESSMENT CHECKLIST

Wants

- [ ] *Produce for home use (e.g. animals and facilities required, crops and land required, wood for fuel, rainwater harvesting, wind power etc.)*
- [ ] *Produce for sale*
- [ ] *Areas for wildlife and plans for conservation*
- [ ] *Facilities for recreation, leisure and play*
- [ ] *Qualities (e.g. space, peace, beauty, views, privacy)*
- [ ] *Overall vision*
- [ ] *Priorities*

Needs

- [ ] *Aspirations (e.g. self-sufficiency, sustainability, making an income)*
- [ ] *Facilities (e.g. consideration for disabilities)*

Resources

- [ ] *Time available for implementation (how much and when)*
- [ ] *Time available for maintenance (how much and when)*
- [ ] *Energy levels, health and fitness (e.g. any disability, plans for retirement)*
- [ ] *Skills*
- [ ] *Money (how much and when)*

5 SURVEY

The next part of the process is a stock-taking one. Your aim is to gather detailed information about every existing aspect of your site which might be relevant to your design. Most of this information will come from the site itself, but you will then need to add to this by talking to people who know the site and by researching printed and online sources.

Site description

The first step is to compile a site description. To do this, you need to observe your site from as many different viewpoints and on as many occasions as possible. Visit every part of the site, and look at its buildings and features from all angles, as well as examining them at close quarters. Observe the site in all weathers – and, if possible, in all seasons. That way, you will know about frost pockets before you plant your fruit trees, or will have monitored wind speeds through the year before siting your wind turbine.

You need to gather information about the site systematically and objectively. Avoid value judgements and the temptation to look for solutions; the aim of this stage in the process is simply to gain an understanding of what is there. Try to start with an open mind; do not assume that you already know what is important, or omit whole areas because you think they have no relevance to your plans. One of the main aims of the site survey is to alert you to possibilities that you have not thought of.

However, do not include irrelevant, obvious or unnecessarily detailed information merely for the sake of it.

Record only what is already there, not your proposals for change. If, however, you know of definite future developments which will affect your site – the removal of a building on an adjoining property, for instance – those should be noted.

If there are things about the site that you cannot work out by looking – the gradient of a slope, for instance – or you make an observation that you do not understand – say that a certain kind of tree is not doing well – note this down as a query, and resist the temptation to guess an answer. Another aim of this stage is to identify gaps in your information and point you towards areas needing further research.

The most obvious way to record your observations is as a written list, but that will not be the best method for everybody. You may prefer to make annotated sketches, or to speak your observations into a tape recorder, or to make a video of the site, recording your observations as the soundtrack. There is no 'correct' way to do it; the right way is the one that works for you.

Landscape character

Identify the overall landscape character of the site, and its different landscape zones. Note the features and elements, like buildings, hedgerows, trees, woodlands and watercourses, which contribute to the landscape's quality and character, or which help to define the different zones. Note any features that have a wider landscape significance: a very tall tree, for instance, that is a local landmark; a section of hedging that forms part of a hedgerow running beyond your land; a historic building; an archeological feature.

Walk the perimeter of your site, and make a note of any significant factors beyond the boundary. This could include adjacent trees, hedgerows, buildings, watercourses or roads.

Note the character of the landscape beyond your boundaries, how your site fits into and contributes to the wider landscape, and whether it is typical of it.

Think about the visual and aesthetic aspects of your site. Note areas of beauty, and areas which are visually unattractive. Note where the key views and viewpoints are, both within your site looking out (viewpoints here will include particular windows of the house), and outside your site looking into it. Note also where there are areas of hidden ground. New developments sited in these areas would be least disruptive to the overall landscape.

Natural features

Record the landform of your site, its height above sea level, and the steepness and aspect of any slopes. These factors will affect your site's cropping potential, and its suitability for animals. Slopes also have implications for soil erosion, and for the possibilities for water collection and storage. The landform will also help you to assess the microclimate of your site, especially with regard to potential frost pockets and areas of shelter from prevailing winds.

Assess your soil, taking samples from every part of your site, as soil can vary widely across even a small site. Determine its composition – sand, silt, clay, or the ideal organic-rich loam. Do a pH test to determine how acidic or alkaline it is, and an NPK test to check the levels of the major soil nutrients. If there is any possibility that there have been additional buildings on your site in the recent past, or that rubbish might have been dumped there, check for rubble or large objects beneath the soil surface by spiking the soil at regular intervals.

Note the sources of water on the site – wells, springs, streams, roofs from which rainwater is or could be collected, and whether the water is clean, available year-round, and free

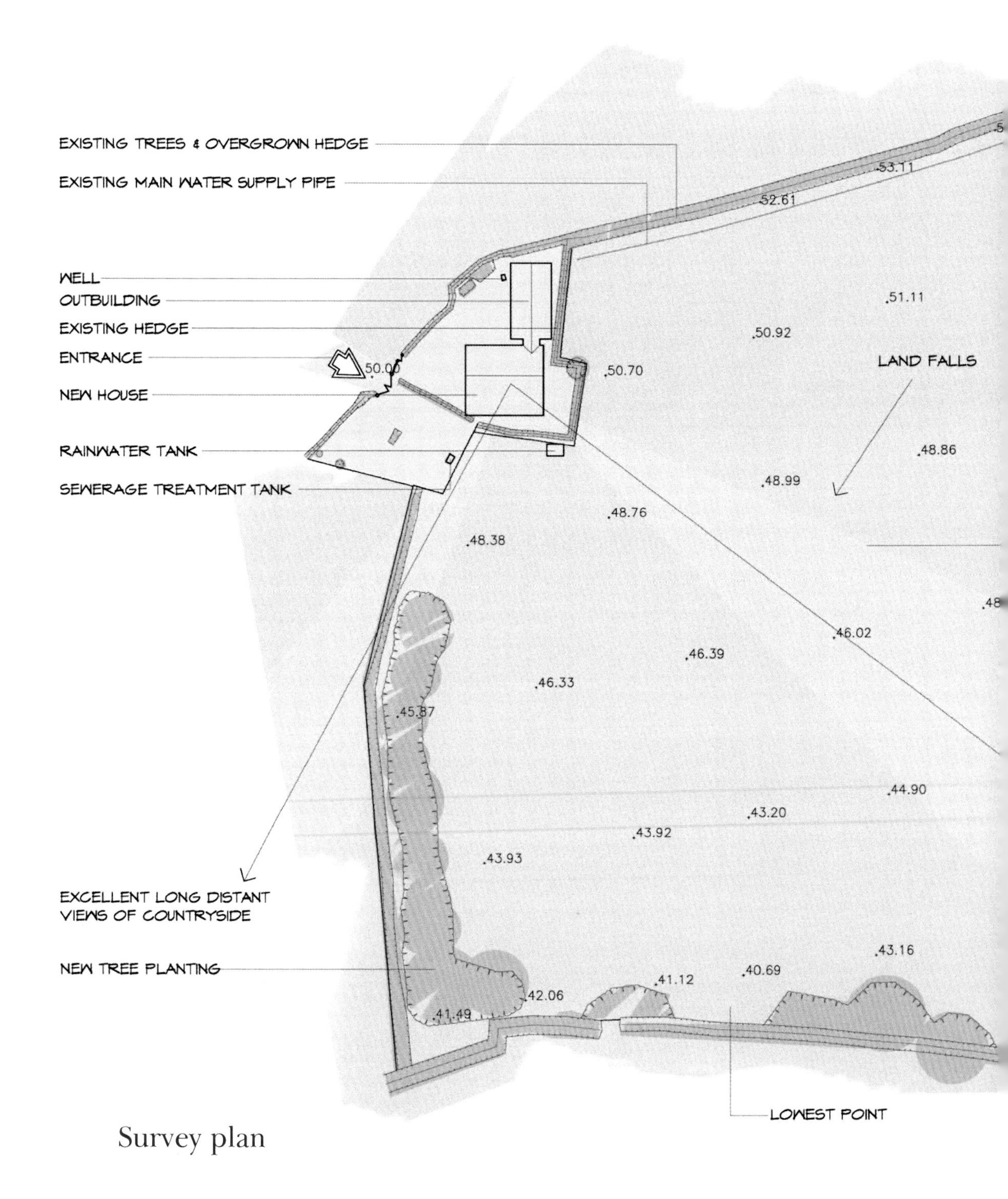
EXISTING TREES & OVERGROWN HEDGE
EXISTING MAIN WATER SUPPLY PIPE
WELL
OUTBUILDING
EXISTING HEDGE
ENTRANCE
NEW HOUSE
RAINWATER TANK
SEWERAGE TREATMENT TANK
EXCELLENT LONG DISTANT
VIEWS OF COUNTRYSIDE
NEW TREE PLANTING
LAND FALLS
LOWEST POINT
53.11
52.61
51.11
50.92
50.00
50.70
48.86
48.99
48.76
48.38
46.02
46.39
46.33
45.87
44.90
43.20
43.92
43.93
43.16
40.69
41.12
42.06
41.49

Survey plan

for you to use. Note also the availability of mains water, including the location of outside taps.

Record the natural flora and fauna of the site: what types of vegetation are growing there, how well they are growing, and what types of animals inhabit or visit the site. These will include both welcome wildlife and problem species like rabbits and slugs.

Built environment

Note each aspect of your built environment, recording the structure (a barn, a wall, a compost bin and so on), what condition it is in, and any additional information that could be useful. For example, note the slope and aspect of roofs, since this has a bearing on their potential for harvesting rainwater and accommodating solar panels, and the aspect of walls, which will determine whether they are suitable for growing fruit against. Note the location of overhead cables and – where these are known – underground cables and pipes; these may affect plans involving tree-planting, building or digging.

Record all the access points and routes into and around the site; the doors to the house and other buildings, the gates into fields, the paths, tracks and driveways, and the access to the site itself. Note the kind of traffic each can take, its state of repair, its steepness, whether it is prone to flooding or is difficult to use in icy weather, and if it is a public right of way. Also note 'desire lines' – tracks which indicate the routes which people and/or animals naturally take between key points on the site, which may deviate from the paths which have been provided.

Maps and plans

Once you have completed your site description, the next step is to draw or commission a map of the site as it is today. This is known as the base map, and it will form the template for all

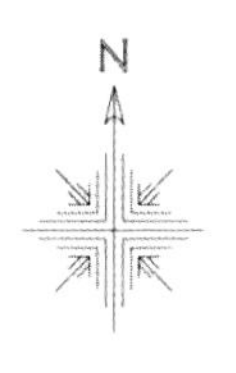

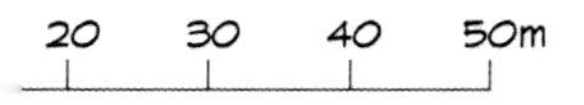

subsequent maps showing design proposals and the final design.

There are a number of reasons why a good base map is essential. Some of these are to do with the process of making it. Mapping a piece of land is one of the best ways of really getting to know it. Drawing a map requires you to visit every part of a site and look at it carefully, and the discipline of drawing an accurate map means that you will see things that you would miss if you were 'just looking'. It also helps you to be objective, which is essential at this 'looking and listening' stage; the technical process of drawing a map helps you to avoid value judgements.

Then there are the benefits of having the finished map. Maps can summarise a great deal of information, as well as providing detail that would be difficult to convey in writing. On a small, simple site, it may be possible to set out the whole of a management plan using maps. A map provides a clear, value-free overview of what exists within a site, and this lets you see the possibilities for development. It provides you with a template which shows you the nature and extent of the space available, and this will allow you to visualise alternative placements for new buildings and features and ensure that your design proposals fit together spatially.

Topographic survey

It is strongly advisable to obtain a plan of the whole site from a qualified surveyor, showing all the existing features and elements of your site, both natural and man-made. Undertaking a topographic survey, except on the very smallest of scales, is beyond the skills of the lay person. A qualified land surveyor will have all the necessary electronic equipment for the production of a complete topological drawing, including aerial images. Employing a professional at this stage will save time and money in the long run, as it ensures that you have a plan which is completely accurate, and in which nothing has been overlooked.

A professional topographic survey will show the boundaries of the site, its existing levels, the location of all physical features such as buildings, trees and rock outcrops, rights of way, access restrictions, and the locations of all utilities such as foul and stormwater sewers, water and gas pipes, and electricity and telephone lines. A second type of survey covers all the natural environmental factors of a site. In certain circumstances specialist environmental surveys may be required, such as

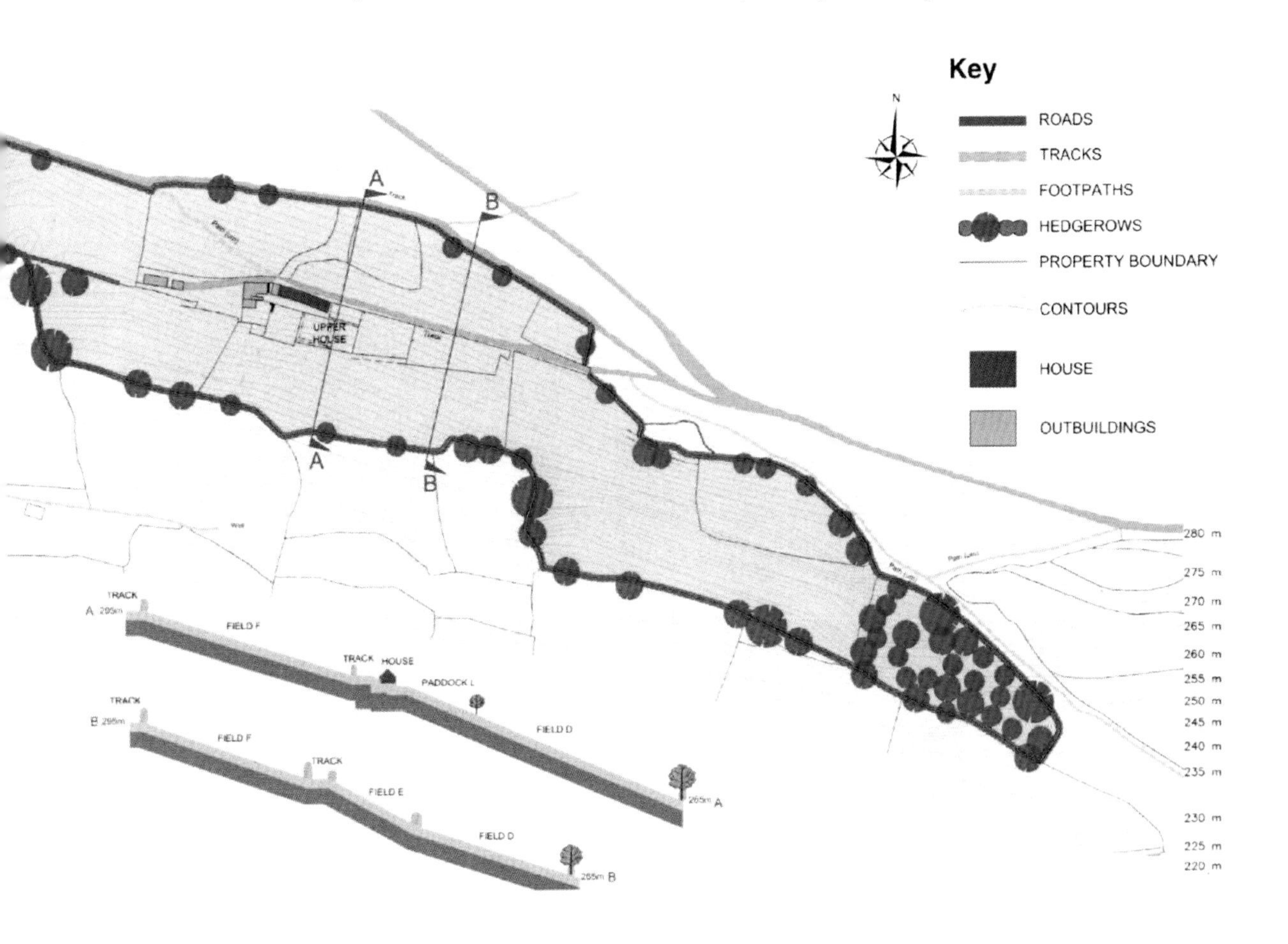

Topographic survey map

ecological and arboricultural ones. A third type of survey concerns the visual and qualitative characteristics of a site. For most smallholding sites all three can be incorporated into one drawing, but it depends on the complexity of the site.

Mapping

If, for whatever reason, you choose not to employ a surveyor, you will need to draw your own base map. You do not, however, need to start from scratch. Scale plans of land are generally supplied as part of the documents when you are buying a property, so if you have your purchase documents to hand you will already have a professionally drawn-up template on which to base your map. If not, outline maps are available from the Ordnance Survey, either on paper or in digital form. Large-scale OS maps may already include some field boundaries and topographical information, but be aware that these may not be accurate or up to date.

Large-scale Ordnance Survey maps, as shown in this example, can be used as a starting point for mapping.

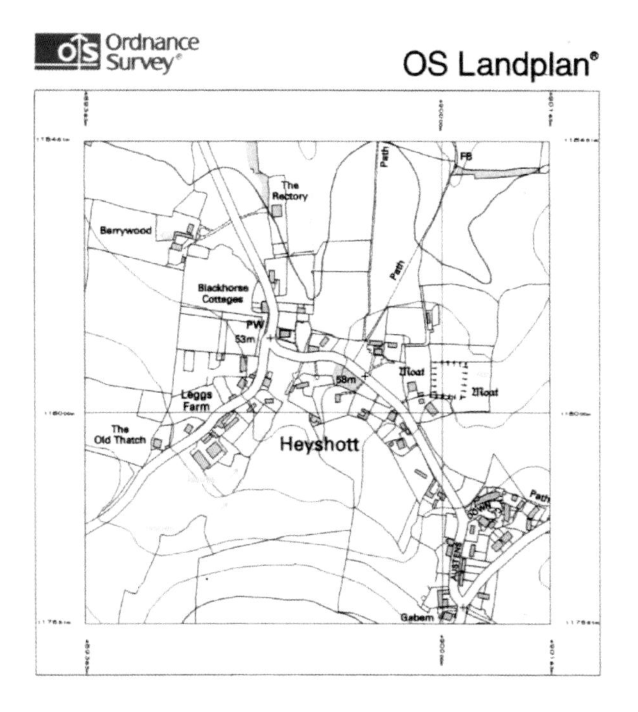

As long as you are using a professionally produced map as a template, you do not need special technical skills or artistic talent to draw a simple map; it is just a question of working as neatly and accurately as possible. Make sure that the dimensions are reasonably accurate, and that all parts of the map are drawn to the same scale. Maps should normally be no bigger than A3. Anything larger is difficult to handle – especially outdoors – and to photocopy.

Only record on the map what is actually there; do not be tempted to include proposed new features on the base map, as that will defeat the object of the exercise. Include only as much detail as will be useful to you; a map needs to provide an immediate picture of the site, and too much detail obscures this. If you need to include a lot of detail in specific areas, like the farmyard, where you will be designing on a metre by metre basis, draw additional larger-scale maps of these areas, rather than cluttering the base map. If it is important to you to record a lot of detail about one or more specific themes, like microclimate or ecology, it may be helpful to record each of these on a transparent overlay which you can lay over your base map.

The base map should include all buildings, roads and paths, watercourses, trees, hedges, areas of vegetation, slopes and other major land features. Include relevant features beyond your site boundaries, like roads, access points, and neighbouring buildings or trees which cast shade or provide shelter.

Research

There will be information you need that you cannot get by looking at the land, and the process of compiling your site description will alert you to things that need further research. In order to complete your survey, you will need to spend some time filling the gaps in your information: checking climate records, for instance, to find out whether current weather conditions are typical, or looking at old maps and photographs to discover the alignment of field boundaries that you wish to restore. As well as using books and the internet, talk to previous owners of your property and to your new neighbours. The store of knowledge they have built up will be invaluable, especially if their families have worked the land for generations.

Obtaining detailed local climatic information can be expensive, and may not be helpful, as the conditions at your local weather station may differ significantly from those on your land. An overview of the local climate will suffice for most purposes: the prevailing wind, the number of hours of sunshine, the annual rainfall and its distribution through the year, the average temperatures, the earliest and latest likely frost dates, the likelihood of snow. If you are considering solar or wind energy systems, or you want to grow a crop or keep a type of animal that is borderline for your area, you should seek professional advice. Remember that the climate is changing, so consult your neighbours for their experience of recent years as well as researching local norms – these may not be normal any more.

Another important thing to research is any legal or environmental designation on your land, and the restrictions it places on what can be done to it. Environmental designations may make grants available, although these will come with stipulations about how they can be used. If the site has not been used for smallholding previously, you need to ensure that this change of use is permissible, and if so, whether there are any restrictions on what kinds of livestock you may keep. If your site is rented rather than owned, you will need to find out what changes you are permitted to make. If you are contemplating building work which will require planning permission, you will need to find out whether the changes you have in mind are likely to be acceptable, and what the application process involves.

You may also want to research any guidance for the area produced by local conservation organisations. Extensive advice on how to design and manage land sustainably is available from local, regional and national conservation organisations, while advice on setting up in smallholding can be obtained from smallholding associations and magazines. Other things you may wish to obtain are local soil maps and local wildlife data. For details, see the 'Further reading' and 'Resources' sections at the end of this book.

SURVEY CHECKLIST

1. Site data

- [ ] *Site name and location*
- [ ] *Six-figure OS grid reference*
- [ ] *Size in total, and of individual compartments or features*
- [ ] *Aspect/compass direction*
- [ ] *Altitude*
- [ ] *Latitude*
- [ ] *Overview of landform and character e.g. hilly, open, wooded*
- [ ] *Cultural, aesthetic and historical considerations e.g. landscape value, cultural associations, historical land use and landscape history, archaeology, historic buildings, sacred sites*
- [ ] *Public benefit and use e.g. recreational use, educational value*

2. Legal data

- [ ] *Tenure and conditions upon it, leases, tenancies, restrictions, mineral rights, licenses etc.*
- [ ] *Access, rights of way etc.*
- [ ] *Designations e.g. SSSI, AONB, listed buildings, monuments*
- [ ] *Zoning for planning purposes*
- [ ] *Grants and conditions upon them*
- [ ] *Easements or legal limitations shown on title or deed*
- [ ] *Other legal considerations affecting the site*

SURVEY CHECKLIST continued

3. Services data

- [ ] *Services/utilities: location:*
  - [ ] *Gas: underground, calor gas*
  - [ ] *Water (underground)*
  - [ ] *Electric (underground or overhead)*
  - [ ] *Telephone (underground or overhead)*
  - [ ] *Sewer/septic tank*
- [ ] *Mains water supply, downpipes, grey water outlets, land drains*

4. Ecological data

- [ ] *Animals: native and introduced, endangered species*
- [ ] *Vegetation: species present and their state of health, invasive or noxious plants, rare species, soil indicators, water indicators, potential uses:*
  - [ ] *Fuel*
  - [ ] *Edible*
  - [ ] *Compostable*
  - [ ] *Valuable to wildlife*
  - [ ] *Other*
- [ ] *Pests*
- [ ] *Diseases*
- [ ] *Human impacts, foot traffic*

5. Natural environmental data

CLIMATE

- [ ] *Rainfall: yearly and monthly averages*
- [ ] *Humidity: yearly and monthly averages*
- [ ] *Wind: prevailing direction(s) and monthly averages*
- [ ] *Temperature: monthly maximum, minimum and average*
- [ ] *Sunshine: average monthly hours*
- [ ] *Frost: average and extreme first and last dates*
- [ ] *Length of growing season*

MICROCLIMATE

- [ ] *Whole site and sub-areas: wind, light, areas of sun and shade, temperature, frost, moisture, combined effects*

GEOLOGY AND SOIL

- [ ] *Clay, sand and/or silt content*
- [ ] *Structure e.g. heavy or light, rich or depleted, stable or slumping*
- [ ] *Organic matter content*
- [ ] *pH*
- [ ] *Nutrients: nitrogen, phosphorus, potassium and trace minerals*
- [ ] *Drainage*

TOPOGRAPHY/LANDFORM

- [ ] *Elevation*
- [ ] *Slopes: erosion potential, air drainage*
- [ ] *Rock outcrops*

SURVEY CHECKLIST continued

WATER

- [ ] *Springs, streams, gullies, ponds, pond sites*
- [ ] *Wells, outside taps, roofs and downpipes*
- [ ] *Water storage sites and containers*
- [ ] *Water table's distance from surface*
- [ ] *Pollution sources and impacts*
- [ ] *Water movement during rain, flooding zones*
- [ ] *Water gravity feed*

6. Physical data

- [ ] *Structures*
- [ ] *Buildings e.g. house, garage, outbuildings: type, condition, appearance, location, impact*
- [ ] *Walls, fences, hedges etc: type, condition*
- [ ] *Access/traffic*
- [ ] *Paths, roads, tracks, footpaths, bridleways, gates, doors, bridges etc: siting, condition, kind of traffic, frequency of traffic, steepness, erosion potential, seasonality*
- [ ] *Desire lines*
- [ ] *Boundaries*
- [ ] *Adjacent features with an impact on the site e.g. neighbouring buildings and trees, roads etc.*

- [ ] *Outside impacts e.g. pollution sources and impacts, noise, potential for crime*
- [ ] *Activities of neighbours that may affect design e.g. land uses, noise, children, pets, visits*
- [ ] *Resources*
- [ ] *Minerals, energy potential etc.*
- [ ] *Resources in neighbourhood e.g. sources of organic matter, soil and building materials, plant and seed sources, sawmills, factories, food processors, stores, landfills*

7. Visual data

- [ ] *General impressions of landform, landscape character etc.*
- [ ] *Zones: different areas of distinct character*
- [ ] *Views from and to neighbours*
- [ ] *Views in different directions*
- [ ] *Eyesores*

6 ANALYSIS

Once you have completed your site observations and research, compiled your site description, and drawn or commissioned your base map, the 'looking and listening' stage of the planning process is complete. It is now time to analyse and evaluate all of the facts about your site, as revealed by the survey and the site description, and to make considered judgements based on your findings. You also need to revisit your aims and requirements and decide how these can best be met, in the light of what you have discovered.

At the end of this evaluation stage, you will be in a position to make sound decisions about your intended objectives for your site, and about the management methods you will use to reach them. You will also be able to decide on the best design for your site.

Evaluation

Reviewing requirements

Now that you have assessed your site, look again at your list of wants and needs. Do they still seem realistic, given what you have discovered about your site? Hopefully this is not the point at which you realise that you have bought the wrong piece of land, but it may be the time to reshape your ambitions to fit the realities on the ground. If, for instance, you wanted to generate wind power, and your survey has found no suitable site for a

The species you might have dreamed of keeping do not always turn out to be the most realistic options.

turbine, but has flagged up the existence of a sloping south-facing roof, this could be the moment to embrace solar power as your way forward.

If you compiled your list of requirements with a family or partner, you now need to discuss any competing and contradictory ideas in the light of the site survey. Armed with the facts, you will be in a better position to assess different ideas for the site, and to decide which are the better propositions. It is difficult to let go of long-held dreams, but you can now be confident that you are making the right decisions about which ideas to pursue, and which to say goodbye to.

Considering the options

Once you have a clear and realistic set of propositions for your site, go back to your site description and base map. Before starting to bring in ideas for change, consider what you already have. It is easy to get caught up in grand plans for change, but it is more sustainable – not to mention cheaper – to modify what is already there. Could existing structures be adapted to new uses? Could you add to existing planting, or replace it gradually, rather than clearing it wholesale? Good design should not be sacrificed on the altar of sustainability, but it is important to remember the 'embodied energy' and ecological value in existing structures and features, and to conserve this where possible.

Work systematically through your list of requirements and the elements in your site description, looking for things which marry up, like a small building which could be adapted to give you a chicken shed, or a sheltered south-facing area of ground which would make a perfect orchard. Look for potential sites for the new structures and features you want to add, and also for points in the site survey which suggest new ideas. If, for instance, the garden is downhill from the house, that would allow you to install a gravity-fed irrigation system using rainwater from the house roof.

If you have identified eyesores on your site, decide whether these need to be removed, improved or screened. You also need to address any problems you have discovered, such as waterlogged areas, access difficulties, planning constraints and so on. This is the moment to work out how these can be remedied so that you can achieve what you want from the site – or how your requirements could be modified to make them achievable.

Try to stay focussed on the big picture before getting down to detail. It is easy to get sidetracked by design details when key decisions have still to be made. There is no point, for instance, in arguing about the dimensions of the duck pond if you might still decide to keep chickens instead. At best, this wastes time on details which later turn out to be irrelevant; at worst, it closes off possibilities which would have emerged as a better option.

A helpful working order to keep in mind is aims, concepts, details. The first step is to finalise your aims: for instance, to extend the existing hedgerows to encircle your site. The second step is to decide on concepts: for instance, to grow only native hedging species, or to choose varieties which will also produce a harvest of nuts and berries. Only then is it time for the third step: the details of exactly what species you will grow, the spacing they will require, how many saplings you will need, which supplier you will obtain them from, and so on.

Natural environmental factors

Consider the natural elements of your site: its landscape features, its flora and fauna, and its visual and aesthetic qualities. Think about how these contribute to the overall appearance and ecological value of the site, and assess what needs to be done to conserve, enhance or change them.

The priority is to conserve and manage existing natural features like hedgerows, copses and ponds. Decide whether these need strengthening – by filling in gaps in hedgerows, for instance, or adding bankside planting to a stream. Only then should you think about adding new natural features, and about how – or indeed whether – these will enhance the landscape. You need to give careful thought to how existing flora and fauna might be affected by the changes you are proposing; it is never safe to assume that any changes you make will be an automatic improvement for biodiversity.

Think especially carefully about natural features that you want to remove. Remember that areas of 'waste' ground can be valuable habitats; the fact that they look untidy to human eyes is often a measure of their value to wildlife. Consider screening a thicket or a swampy area with additional planting, rather than succumbing to the urge to tidy it away.

You will need to balance your plans for conservation with your need for a practical working smallholding, but with careful planning, the two can happily co-exist. If you know your plans will detract from the wildlife value of one area – say, for instance,

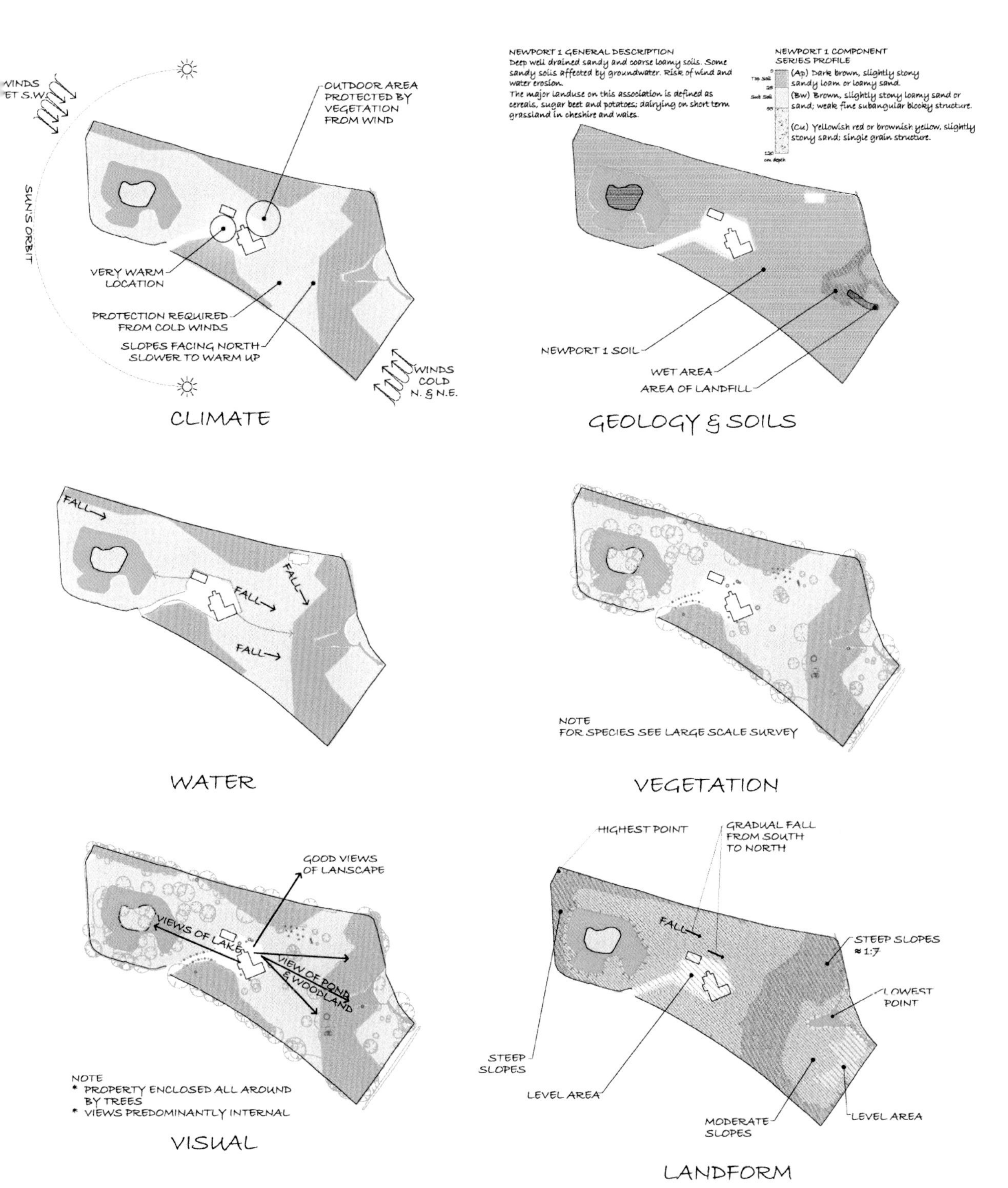

Natural environmental factors

that creating a vegetable plot will necessitate the removal of a mature tree that is casting shade – consider whether you can repay this by improving the ecology of another area – by, for instance, linking two sections of hedgerow to create a wildlife corridor. *See Appendix 1: Table of landscape elements.*

Analysis plan

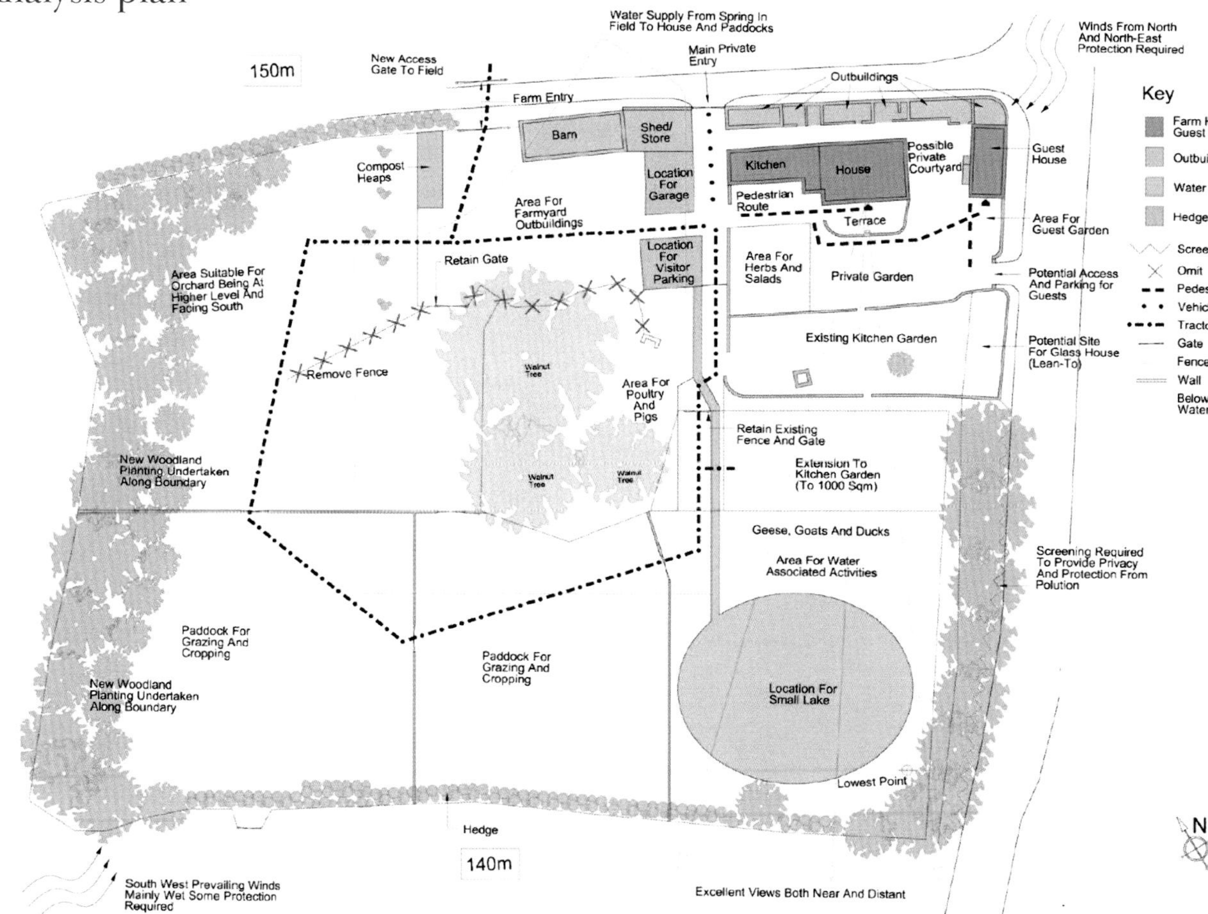

Objectives

Once the analysis of your site data is complete and you have considered all of your options in detail, it is time to choose between them, decide which of your ideas you wish to pursue, and formulate objectives for your site.

'Objectives' is the name given to the proposals that you decide to implement, and set out how each of your intentions for the site will be realised. For an eco-smallholding it is generally helpful to organise your objectives into three categories: farmed land, infrastructure, and natural areas, encompassing grasslands, wetlands and woodlands. Objectives may be long-term, reflecting your overall intentions for the site, or short-term, describing how specific projects will be implemented, or how particular aspects of the site are to be developed.

If, for instance, you decide that one of your long-term objectives is to grow enough trees to be self-sufficient in fuel, the related short-term objectives might identify the area of ground where you will plant the trees and the corner of the farmyard where you will build a wood-store, state which species you intend to grow, and note that secure fencing will be required to protect young trees from the sheep in the adjacent field. They might also note the number of trees you intend to plant over each of the next ten years, and the quantity of wood you expect to harvest, with projected dates by which you hope to be self-sufficient in fuel for heating and cooking.

You will probably need to undertake more research at this stage to flesh out the details of your objectives. Having taken the decision to plant hedges, for instance, you will now need to research suitable species and varieties. If you intend to produce enough of a particular commodity for self-sufficiency, or to have a surplus to sell, you will need to work out the yields you can expect from a given area of ground or number of stock. Where you need to buy plants or stock, you will need to research possible suppliers, get estimates of the cost, and select the best option. Once these details have been worked out, they can be added to your management plan as short-term objectives, enabling you to work towards your long-term objectives for your site.

7 DESIGN

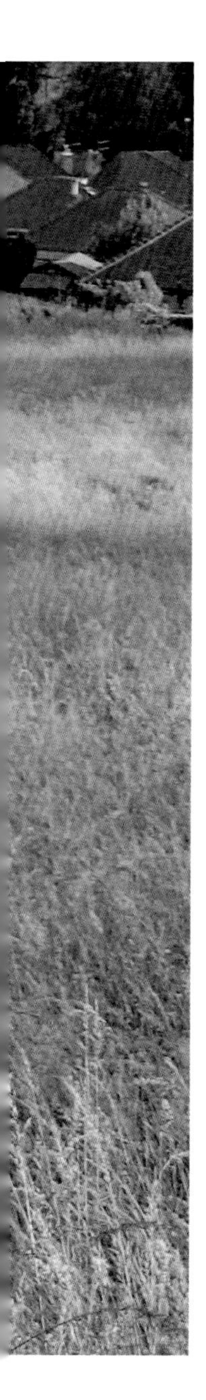

Once you have finalised your objectives, you will know what elements – buildings, fences, plots, trees and so on – are required to make them a reality. This means that you are now in a position to design your landscape.

Designing with nature

If you force an unsuitable design on a landscape, you are working against nature – and this is not an easy thing to do. You can only keep an unsuitable design functioning by investing large amounts of work, energy and money in it. High inputs run counter to the principles of ecological design, and they cannot be sustained in the long term; eventually human energy will wane, money will run out, or global resources like oil will run dry. At this point nature will reclaim the landscape.

If, instead, you design a landscape that meshes with the natural ecology of a site, nature will support it. It will need minimal inputs from non-renewable energy sources, and the human inputs it requires will be at a manageable level. So rather than trying to change your site to accommodate your plans, you should let the site inspire the choice and placing of the elements in your design.

The place to put a lawn, for instance, is a flat, open space where the soil is neither parched nor waterlogged. Putting it where the ground is uneven will require major earthworks, a steep site will be difficult to mow, putting it under trees will

Overview sketch

mean constant work to clear away leaves and rake out moss, and so on. If you cannot provide a suitable site for a lawn, a better way forward is to consider alternatives, like an area of native grasses which are allowed to grow long, a wildflower meadow, or paving interplanted with shade-tolerant plants. These will look much better with much less care.

Species that grow naturally in your area are adapted to your local conditions, so they are far more likely to thrive with minimal attention than exotic species. The fertility of your soil can (and should) be improved with regular applications of compost or manure, but you should regard its chemical and physical make-up as a given. Choose plants that are adapted to your existing soil conditions, rather than trying to alter the soil to suit the plants.

Connections, zones and sectors

Making connections

So far, you will have created lots of lists – lists of what you want, of what you need, and of what is already there; lists of structures, of plants, of tasks, of functions. Now you need to think about how these separate elements could be combined to create a living landscape.

A natural ecosystem is self-contained and self-sustaining; it produces all of its own fertility and recycles all of its waste, and sunlight provides all of the energy needed to power it. Every niche is occupied, and everything is interconnected, with one species' waste becoming another species' food. The aim of ecological design is to mimic the interconnectedness of a natural landscape. This lets you create a sustainable system which needs few or no inputs, produces little or no waste, uses little or no non-renewable energy, and produces the best possible yields with the least possible labour.

Ecological design aims to place elements in the best possible relationship to one another. The ideal is for every plant or structure in a design to have its needs met as far as possible by other design elements, and for it to help to meet the needs of other elements. Each productive linkage between elements means less work for you – and each byproduct which you find a use for means less waste.

Think about possible connections between the different

elements in your lists, both those that already exist and those you want to add. Consider what each element needs in order to thrive, what would be harmful to it and needs to be kept away, what it could offer to other elements in the design, and what they could offer it.

An apple tree, for instance, needs shelter, sunshine and good soil; when mature, it offers shelter, shade and a habitat for wildlife, as well as providing food and creating beauty for people. Think about where its needs would best be met, and where it might be most useful to other elements in your design. Look for other items in your lists that could helpfully be placed alongside it – an underplanting of wild flowers, for instance, to enhance its wildlife value, or a garden seat, to create a shady place for you to rest. Making the right connections will create a low-maintenance landscape – ensuring the presence of plenty of beneficial insects around your apple tree, for instance, will mean that you have fewer pest control issues to deal with.

Zones

A useful principle when working on the layout of your site is that of zones, a concept from permaculture design. Looking for connections between every pair of elements in your design is clearly not practicable, and the concept of zones helps to structure the process. Zones can be used to help decide where to place the elements of your design so that they work with each other – and in relation to you – in the most effective and efficient way.

Zones can be visualised as a set of concentric circles (although of course they will be less geometrically tidy in practice, being shaped by the topography of your site). The underlying principle is that the things you use most, or which need your attention most often, should be sited closest to hand. The innermost zone is the one you visit most frequently and

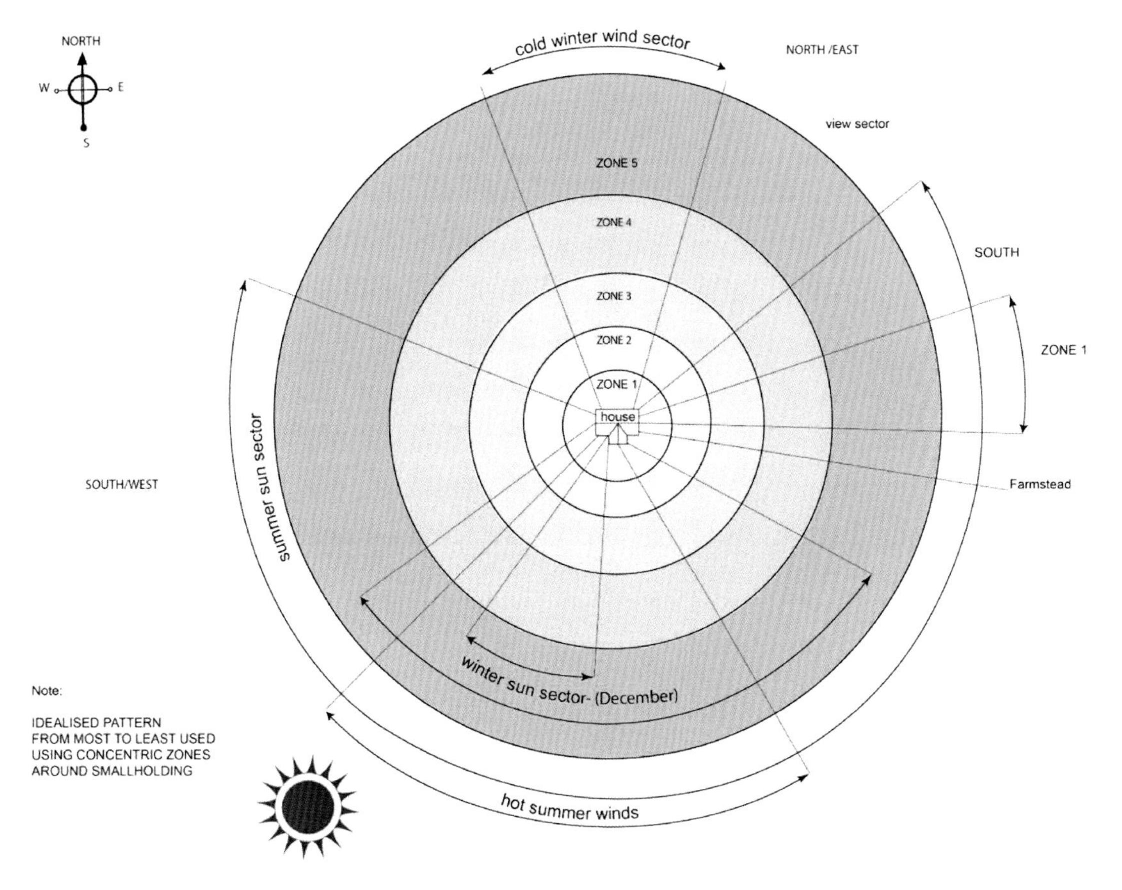

Sector drawing of zones

manage most intensively. Each successive zone requires a lower level of input.

In a typical design, zone 1 contains the house and its immediate environs; it is the zone for living accommodation, ornamental gardens, lawns, car parking and recreational facilities. Into zone 2 go elements needing frequent attention, observation or input: small animals, poultry, vegetable beds and greenhouses. Zone 3 contains fields for crops, orchards, and grazing for lower-maintenance animals, while zone 4 is a semi-wild area containing woodlands, wetlands, meadows and wildlife habitats.

The design for a smaller property might work with only two or three zones, while a larger property might distinguish between managed wildlife habitats in zone 4, and a zone 5 containing areas left entirely to nature. Other systems start with the house in zone 0, and work out from there. What goes into each zone is also flexible, depending on your personal needs and wants. If you are a passionate wildlife gardener, for instance, you might choose to put your wild bird feeding station into zone 1, so you can bird-watch from the house.

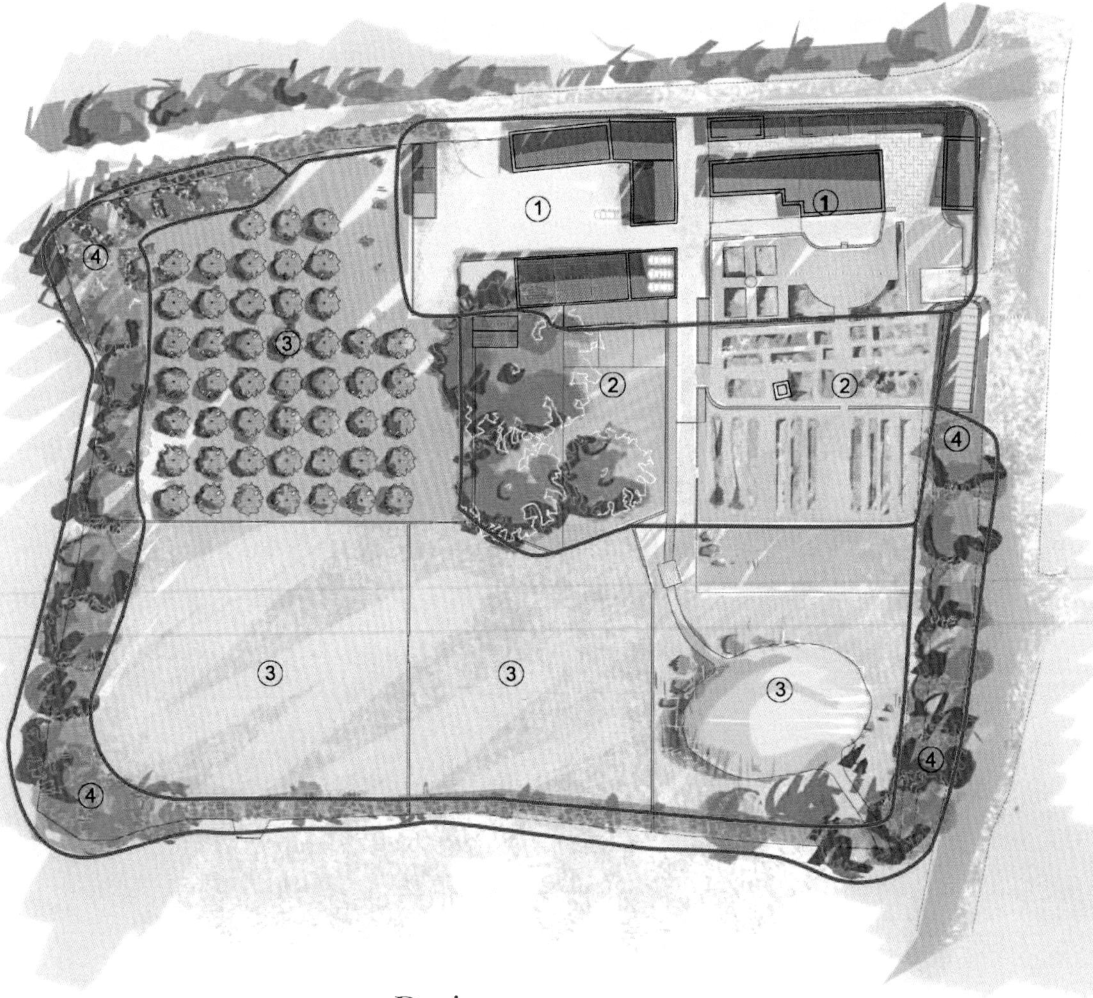

DESIGN ZON

ZONE 1
HOUSE
GARAGE
ORNAMENTAL GAF
RECREATION

ZONES 2
SMALL ANIMALS, F
VEGETABLES, HEF
POTECTED CROP
SMALL FRUIT

ZONE 3
FIELD CROPS
ANIMAL GRAZING
LARGE FRUIT ORC

ZONE 4
WOODLAND - FIRE
WETLAND - AQUA

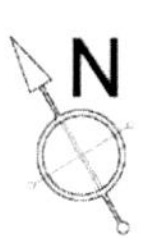

Design zones

Thinking along these lines lets you plan your landscape in an ergonomic way. It also addresses the potential conflict between a smallholding as a place to work and a place to live. A country property can be a wonderful home, but it is all too easy for the noise, dirt and smell of a working farm to invade the house. Thinking in terms of zones lets you create a separate space for living, while establishing convenient access to the smallholding.

When designing the layout of your site, it is helpful to start at the house and work outwards, one zone at a time. This allows you to structure and simplify the process of making connections, and helps you to find the right ones. *See Appendix 2: Zone system contents and uses.*

Sectors

There is a further set of factors to consider. The elements in your design need to be placed in the right relation to one another, and to you, but they also need to be correctly placed in relation to the 'wild energies' flowing into the site. These include sunlight, wind and water, and other less obvious things like pollution (such as fumes or noise) and crime (such as vandalism or theft). Permaculture design describes these things as 'sectors'. A 'sector diagram' outlines the directions from which you can expect these energies, which can be potentially beneficial or potentially harmful.

The elements in a design can interact with sectors in two ways. They can collect or channel energy for use – as, for example, a greenhouse does, or a wind turbine – or they can block or screen sector energies, like a windbreak does. Sometimes an existing aspect of the site will block a sector in a way that is not helpful – a hedge, for instance, that casts shade on your proposed vegetable garden – so your design will need to take account of this by planning to remove or modify it. A good design will place

Owner's layout for medium holding, 5-10 acres

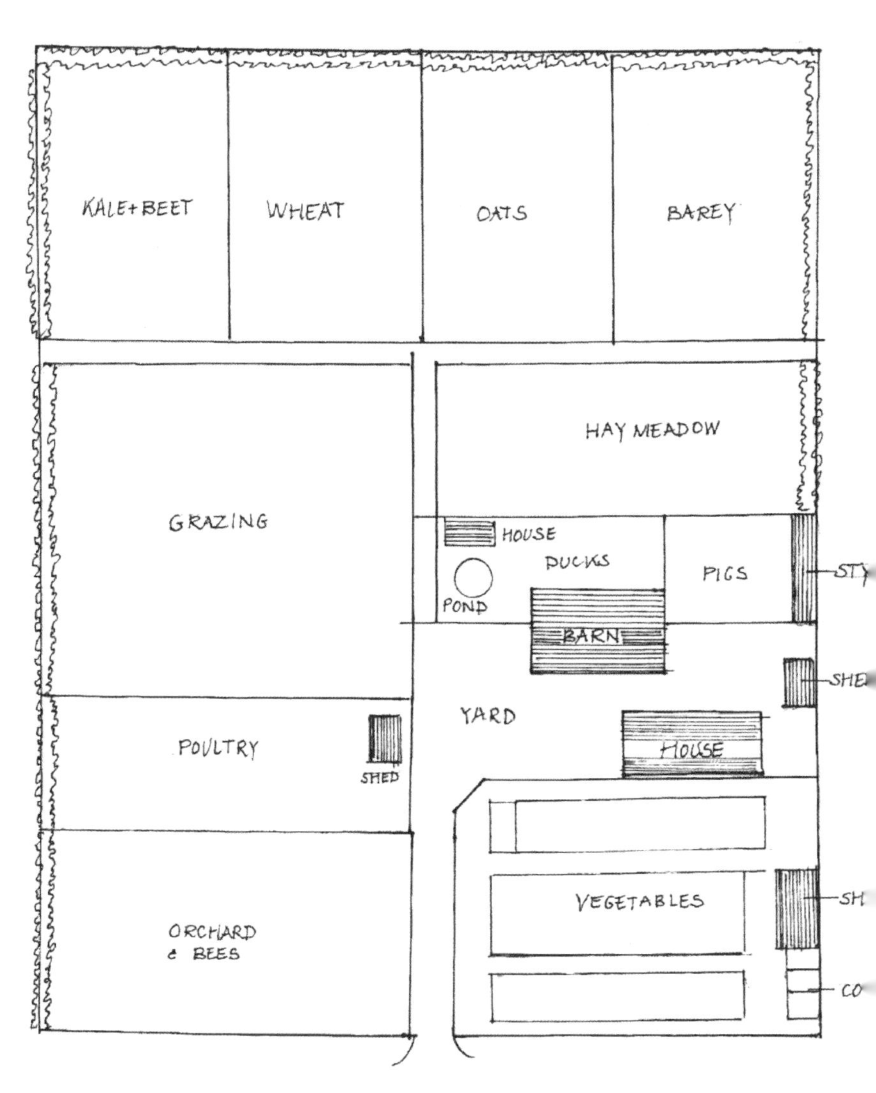

elements to take advantage of positive sector energies and to avoid negative ones. So, for instance, you might site an orchard so that it benefits from a south-facing aspect, or align a barn so that animals and workers will be protected from a northerly wind.

Used together, connections, which place elements in a design in relation to one another, zones, which place them in relation to you, and sectors, which place them in relation to energies from outside the site, can help you design your site to make optimum use of the potential interactions between its different elements.

Layouts

Once you have worked out the optimum connections between the elements in your design, you will know, in principle, where they need to be placed, in relation to one another and the existing elements of your site. It is now time to decide on the layout.

Using your base map as a template, sketch in the various new structures and features in your design – vegetable plot, greenhouse, chicken shed, walls, fences, trees and so on – and erase any existing elements that you have decided to remove. On the first draft, start with rough outlines of just the major components. Then, in subsequent drafts, refine this until you are happy that you have arrived at the best functional layout. Work in pencil rather than pen, so that you can rub out and redraw as necessary.

Where you can see a number of possible options for a layout, make several photocopies of the base map and sketch the different options on to them. Seeing the possibilities is much better than visualising them, and this approach is particularly helpful when a decision is being made collectively. Presenting people with alternatives for discussion draws them more actively into the planning process, and provides a springboard for further ideas.

There is no need for artistic merit in these provisional sketches, but it is important to ensure that you are working to scale and that dimensions are accurate, or you risk devising a layout which will not fit together on the ground. Make sure, for instance, that you are allowing enough space between fruit trees, and that you have measured the space for structures like greenhouses accurately.

Once you are happy with the functional layout, it is time to work on the conceptual layout of specific elements in your

Owner's layout for small holding, 2-5 acres

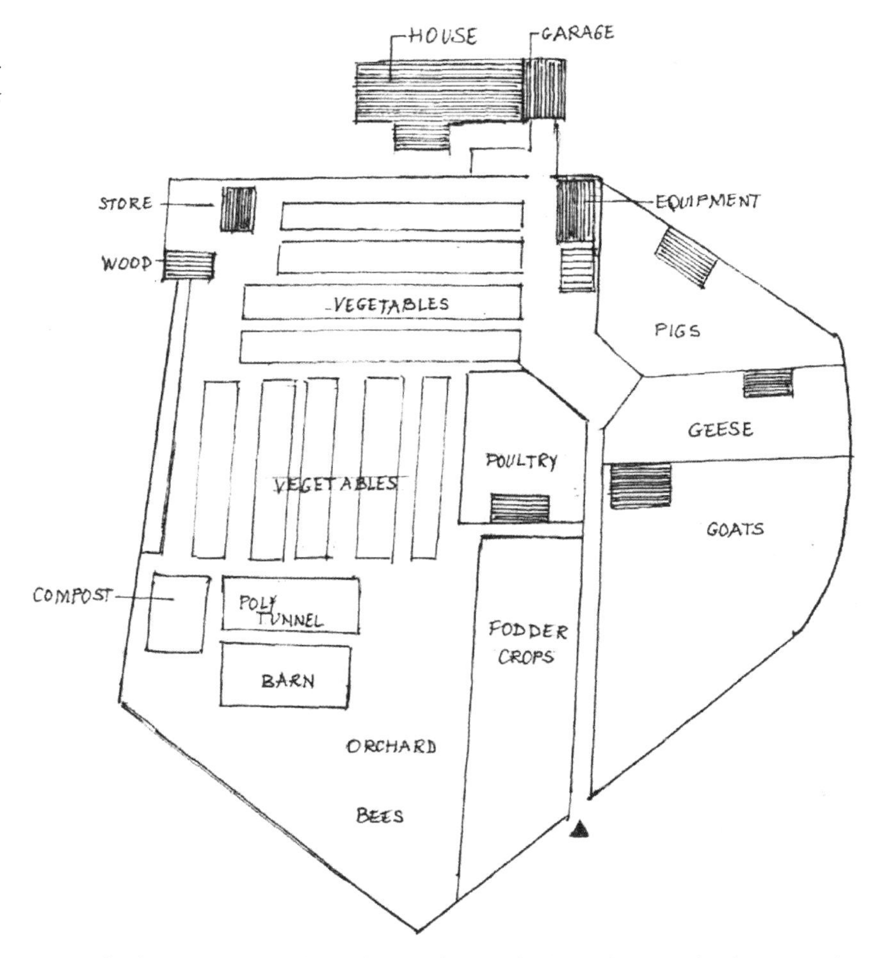

design. You need to think about design themes before getting down to detail. In a vegetable garden, for instance, one possible design theme would be a traditional plot, with straight rows of crops. Another would be a potager, with geometric beds and crops laid out in aesthetically pleasing patterns, while another would be an interplanted plot with fruit, vegetables and flowers all mixed together. You would need to choose between these three design themes – and any other possibilities that appeal to you – before getting into the detail of exactly how the plot is going to be laid out.

When you feel that you have arrived at the best functional and conceptual layouts, make a preliminary design drawing. Where a designer is working on behalf of others, this is then presented to the clients for their feedback. Where you are designing for yourself, or your family, this is the moment to pause, reflect, consult and discuss, to ensure that everyone is really happy with all aspects of the design.

Once you are satisfied, make a final design drawing. This will serve both as a guide as you implement your design, and as inspiration, letting you see the site in its finished glory. If you have the skills and the time, you may want to make a professional-quality drawing, but this is not essential. All you

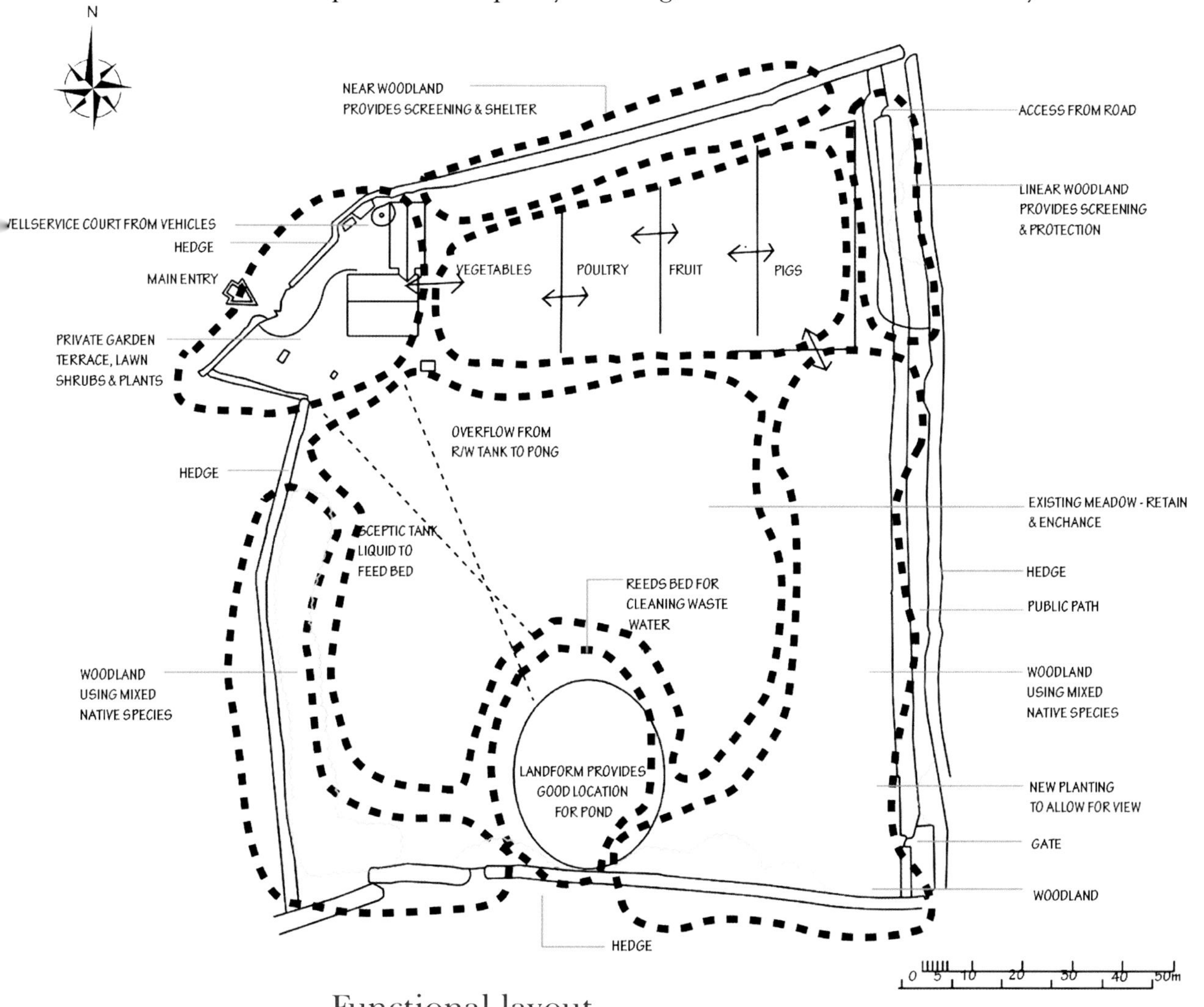

Functional layout

need is a finished design drawing that is neat, clear and easy to interpret, even after some time has elapsed. Do not make the mistake of relying on your memory! Make sure that you include distances, that everything is to scale, and that you record all the detail that you will need to implement the design. If your design proposals are complex, or the design is to be implemented over a number of years, it is helpful to make a series of drawings, one showing each stage of the design.

Depending on the nature of your design, you may need to produce additional drawings relating to specific aspects of it. If

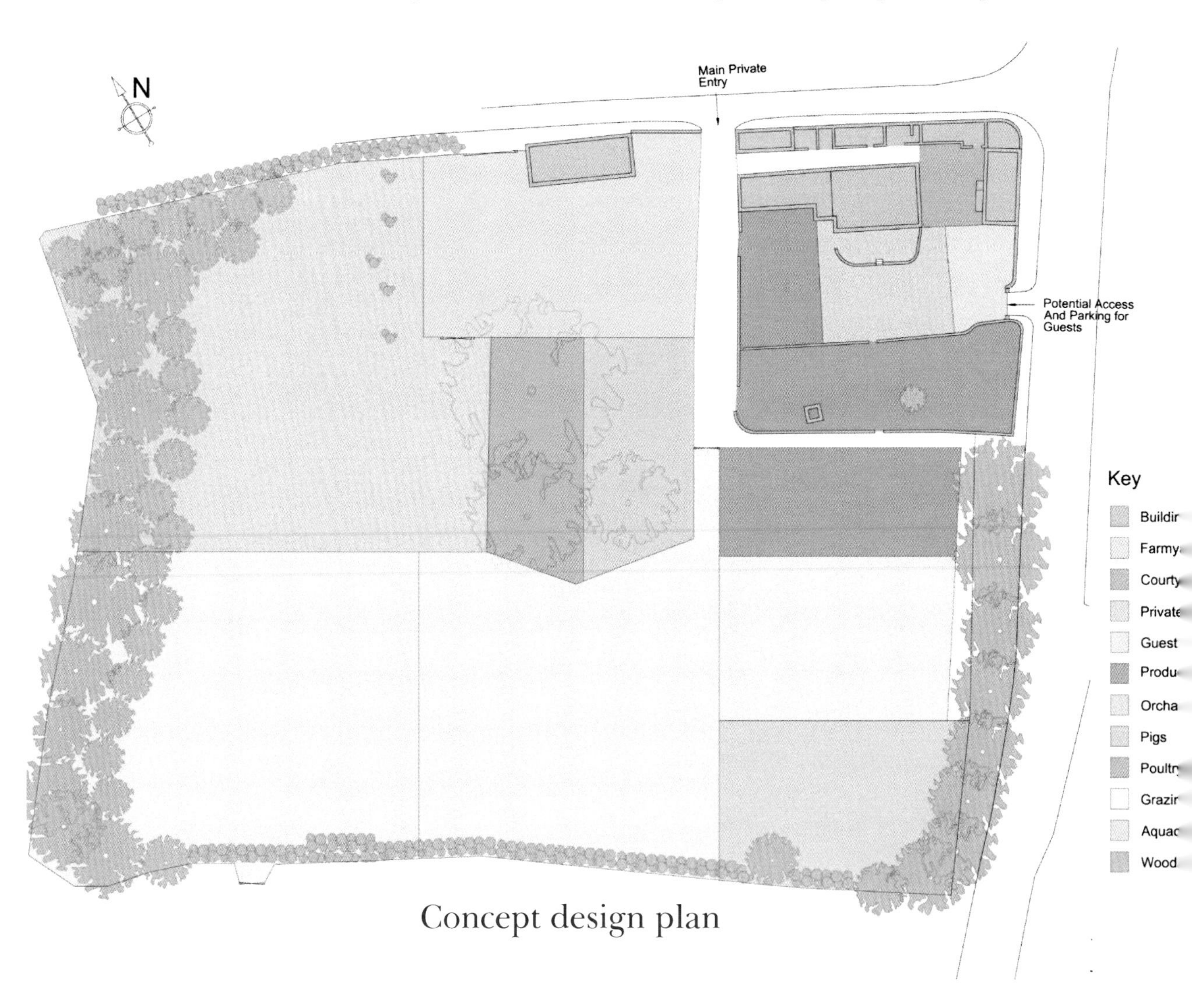

Concept design plan

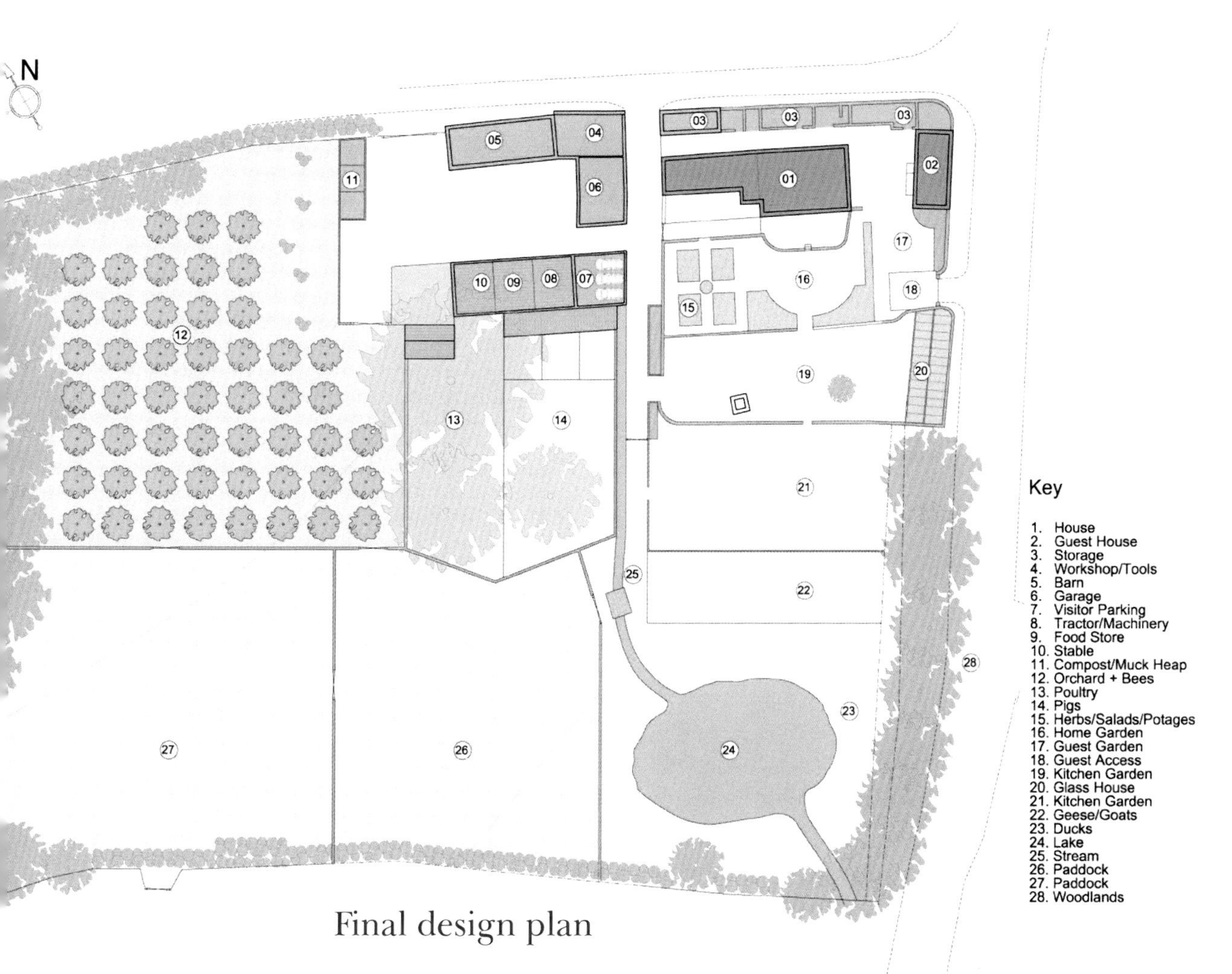

Final design plan

you are proposing to make major changes to the topography of the site, a grading plan will establish locations and levels for buildings, tracks, retaining walls, parking areas and so on. A separate construction plan will provide a key for all the individual elements of the project, such as paths, steps, kerbs, channels, drains, paving patterns, walls and fences. These can be shown in detail on separate section and elevation drawings. A planting plan will locate and identify all plants to be used, and any existing plants that are to be preserved or removed. A plant list, specifying quantities, sizes and varieties, can be included on this drawing or be shown as a separate list.

8 IMPLEMENTATION

Now that you have decided on your objectives and finalised your design, you are in a position to develop your site in the best possible way. The real test of a management plan, however, is how it works in practice. A plan is a tool, not an end in itself – but it is all too easy for the process to stall with the successful completion of the design. The way to avoid this is to include a final section in your plan which sets out how it will be implemented.

The work plan

You now need to organise your intentions into a work plan. This details the work that needs to be done to achieve your objectives and implement your design. It will specify in what order the tasks will be done, when they will be done, how, and (if applicable) by whom.

The first step is to split the work up into individual projects. This is important; viewed as a whole, a completed management plan can seem like a huge undertaking, and all too often excellent plans never get implemented because they seem too daunting. Once you have broken your plan down into manageable projects, it will immediately seem much more achievable. You then need to describe each project and decide who will undertake it. If you intend to employ someone to undertake a particular project, it will need to be precisely specified and costed to ensure that you get exactly what you want, and at the price you expect.

Orchards are an ideal location for all kinds of poultry, as they enjoy the plentiful supply of grubs to be found there.

The next step is to work out a timetable. The ordering of projects can be important, because some things need to be done in a certain order or at certain times. For example, a windbreak needs to be planted in autumn or early spring, and it needs to be established before the fruit trees it is designed to shelter can be planted. You also need to decide what your priorities are. Your most immediate need might, for instance, be a vegetable garden – or it might be an area for relaxation where you can recharge your energies while working on the rest of the design. If your plans involve work requiring heavy machinery, major earth-moving or building, this should be done as early as possible to avoid disturbance or damage to other parts of the design later on. Trees, shrubs and hedging should be planted as soon as possible, so that they can be putting on growth while the rest of the design takes shape around them.

The length of time you allow yourself to complete all the projects is also important. You may not have the time, energy or budget to implement your design all at once, and the job may need to be spread over several months or, with a bigger plan, a number of years. It is unwise to overstretch yourself; your initial enthusiasm will be tested if you take on too much, too quickly, and you need to allow for the other demands on your time.

It is important to find a balance between maintenance and progress tasks. You need to allow yourself enough time to carry out the daily tasks required by your existing smallholding activities, and cyclical tasks like lambing or harvesting, alongside the time needed to implement your design. It makes sense to schedule building and conservation work for times of year when your crops and/or livestock need less attention. It may be helpful to include maintenance tasks within your implementation plan, to ensure that you have allowed sufficient time and resources for everything.

Pigs are useful animals to incorporate into the early stages of a smallholding, as they can easily clear the ground of any unwanted vegetation.

Budgeting and resources

Financial planning

Budgeting or financial planning involves estimating how much money is needed to carry out your work plan, obtaining that money (if necessary), and then accounting for its use. You will already have worked out broadly how much you are able to invest in the whole project at the assessment stage. Now that you have compiled a detailed work programme, you can estimate the required expenditure for each individual project.

You may need to make several estimates, adjusting the specifications and getting different quotations, until you come up with a realistic budget. If you discover that the cost of your plans is beyond your budget, you will need to revisit earlier stages of the plan and make adjustments as necessary; alternatively, you may need to consider implementing your plan over a longer period.

Detailed financial estimates may be required when income and expenditure need to be forecast precisely, for example as part of a business plan. If you are applying for a bank loan, or for grant aid, you may need to compile a separate, formal financial plan, setting out your financial position at the start of the plan and forecasting the net costs of implementing it, alongside any income you anticipate.

When making financial plans, it is advisable to keep some money in reserve in case unforeseen costs arise, or the income from your smallholding falls short of your forecast. Estimating the cost of projects accurately can be difficult, although you may be able to base your estimates on your own previous experience, or that of others.

When drawing up your budget, it is helpful to identify operating income and expenditure separately from major project expenditure and regular fixed costs such as insurance.

Income that you are not yet certain of, such as grant aid, should also be shown separately. This allows you to work out your 'normal' operating profit or loss.

Resources

You also need to determine the resources, other than money, that you will require in order to implement your work plan. You may need new skills, which will mean undertaking the necessary training, or special equipment, which you will need to buy, hire or borrow. You may need help, whether that means employing a specialist contractor to install solar panels, or enlisting a team of friends to dig a pond. You may also need to research suppliers of the materials you require. If you have not previously dealt with the suppliers you are considering, talk to people who have; there is no substitute for personal recommendation.

Monitoring and review

There is no real end point to ecological design, and an important part of any plan is to constantly reevaluate it. As you implement your design and start living with it, you may see improvements which can be made, or you may need to modify it as circumstances change. This can be an additional reason for implementing a design over a number of years.

It is essential to review your plan regularly to ensure that you are achieving your objectives, and to monitor your progress to ensure that your implementation programme is on schedule and within budget. Regular monitoring of the site will help you to assess whether your objectives are being met, and to decide whether your original plans need to be modified or added to.

When you are working in harmony with nature, a design for a site is a living thing, and it will continue to evolve for as long as you live there. There will never be a point at which you can say that your work is finished – but that is part of the joy of it.

9 CONCLUSION

Setting out to create a thriving smallholding which is also sustainable, and which is productive but also gives you a congenial way of life, is not an easy undertaking. There will be challenges and setbacks, and at times it will seem as though there are hard choices to be made between aesthetics and practicality, or between ethics and affordability. But with careful planning and design, what seems impossible at the outset can become a reality. Nature is a powerful partner in ecological design, and if you make ecologically informed choices, nature will support them. Successful, sustainable smallholding is about looking, listening, making the right plans, and putting them in place.

The rewards of doing so are huge. Creating a sustainable smallholding system will allow you to live in a beautiful, biodiverse landscape. It will give you the time and the space to live as well as work, and you will have the satisfaction of knowing that, in your small piece of the world, all is as well as you can make it. Designing in harmony with nature does not cost the earth – it saves it for everyone!

10 CASE STUDIES

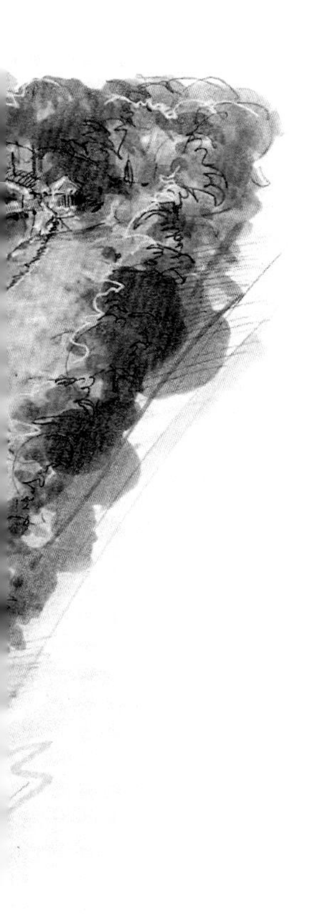

The Birches

The property:

The Birches Smallholding covers two hectares (five acres) of relatively flat land with many trees, predominantly silver birch. The surrounding landscape is gentle rolling farmland interspersed with woodland.

The brief:

To produce a management plan that considered all aspects of sustainability and conservation while allowing the owners to achieve a degree of self-sufficiency. One of them is disabled, so it also included the specific requirement that the design should

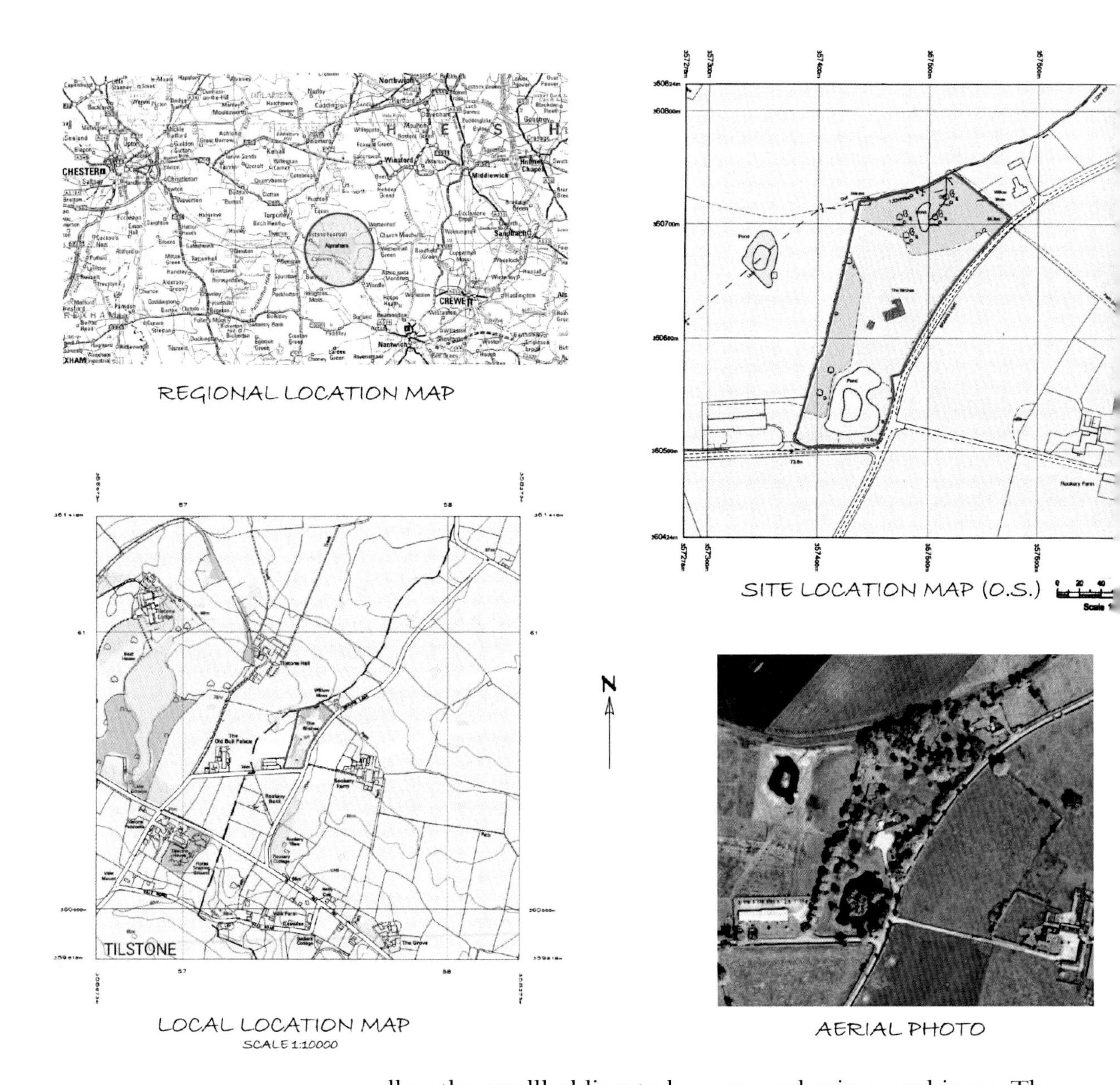

REGIONAL LOCATION MAP

SITE LOCATION MAP (O.S.)

LOCAL LOCATION MAP
SCALE 1:10000

AERIAL PHOTO

allow the smallholding to be managed using machinery. The owners wanted to create areas for the growing of food and the rearing of poultry, to grow timber for fuel, and to create a mosaic of wildlife habitats covering wetland, grassland and woodland. They also wanted to build a natural swimming pool, and to create areas for entertainment and relaxation.

The plan:

The site falls into three areas. The central area around the house, which was designated Zone 1, was clearly the place for recreational and leisure uses, and for a vegetable and herb garden. (Note that the word 'zone' simply means 'area' here and does not relate to the permacultural concept of zones discussed in Chapter 7.) The biggest issue here was the area in front of the house, which needed to become much more defined and welcoming. My plan proposed creating an entry court, with low hedges on either side of a driveway leading into a turning circle of coloured block paving. This would become a hub, with a main path leading to the front entrance of the property and smaller paths leading to other areas.

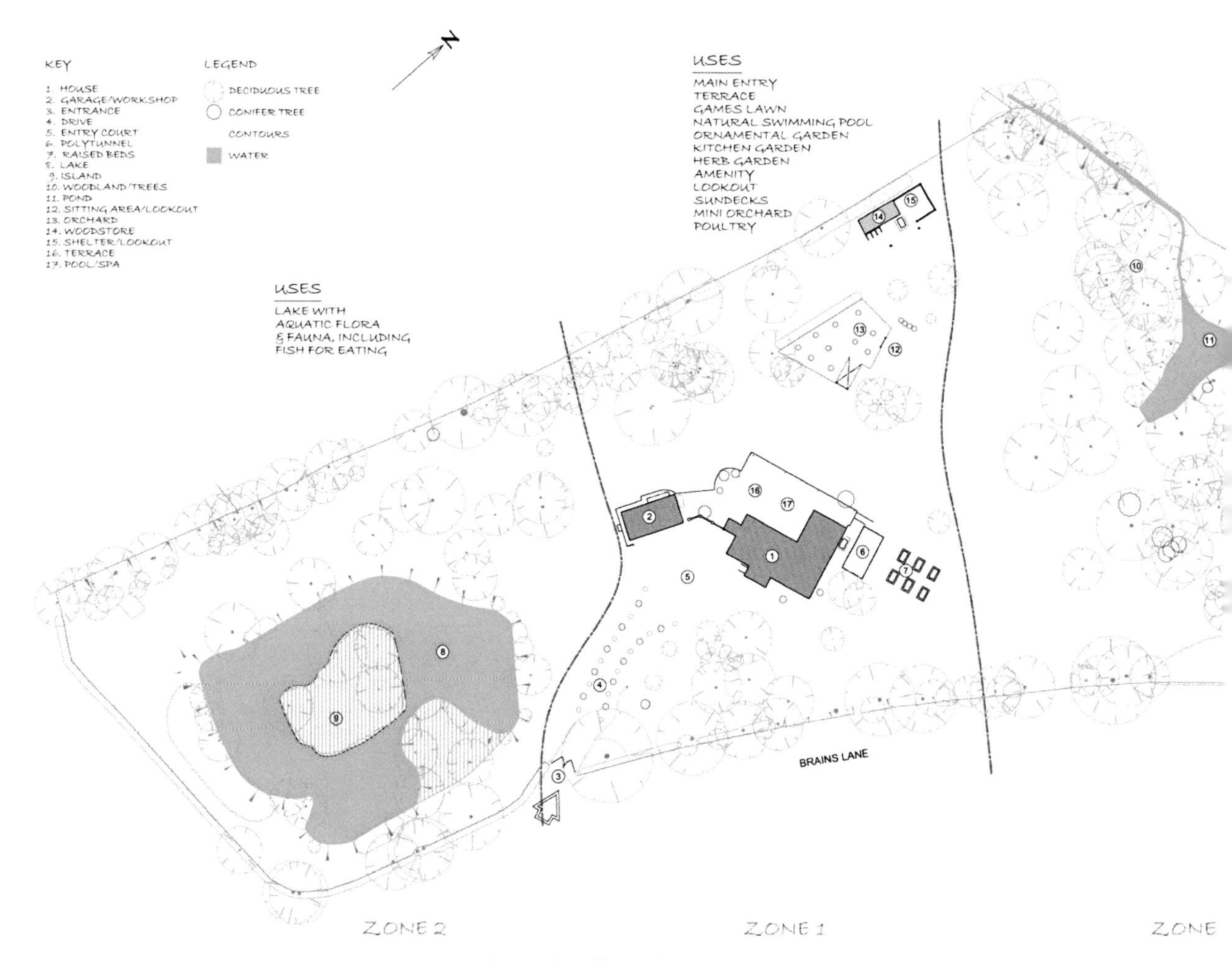

Drawing indicating zones

The existing large rear terrace offered opportunities for outdoor dining, sunbathing and barbecues, and it was proposed that the natural swimming pool should be built nearby. I recommended the removal of the small enclosed orchard to introduce a feeling of spaciousness to the area.

The design proposed that the new kitchen garden should consist of raised beds separated by gravel paths approximately 1.8m (6ft) wide; these would provide a firm surface and sufficient width to admit light machinery and equipment into the garden. Alongside the existing polytunnel, space was allocated for several timber buildings for functions such as a potting shed, a workshop and storage. The poultry area was located next to the kitchen garden for ease of access. A new orchard was planned further from the house, with the trees in two rows to form a small avenue.

Zone 2 is the area to the south of the property containing a lake, trees and a large expanse of mown grass. It was proposed that the lake should be enlarged, reshaped and made deeper, so that it would have a greater impact on the landscape and be much more attractive to wildlife such as moorhens, coots and ducks; some fish could also be reared for eating. I proposed

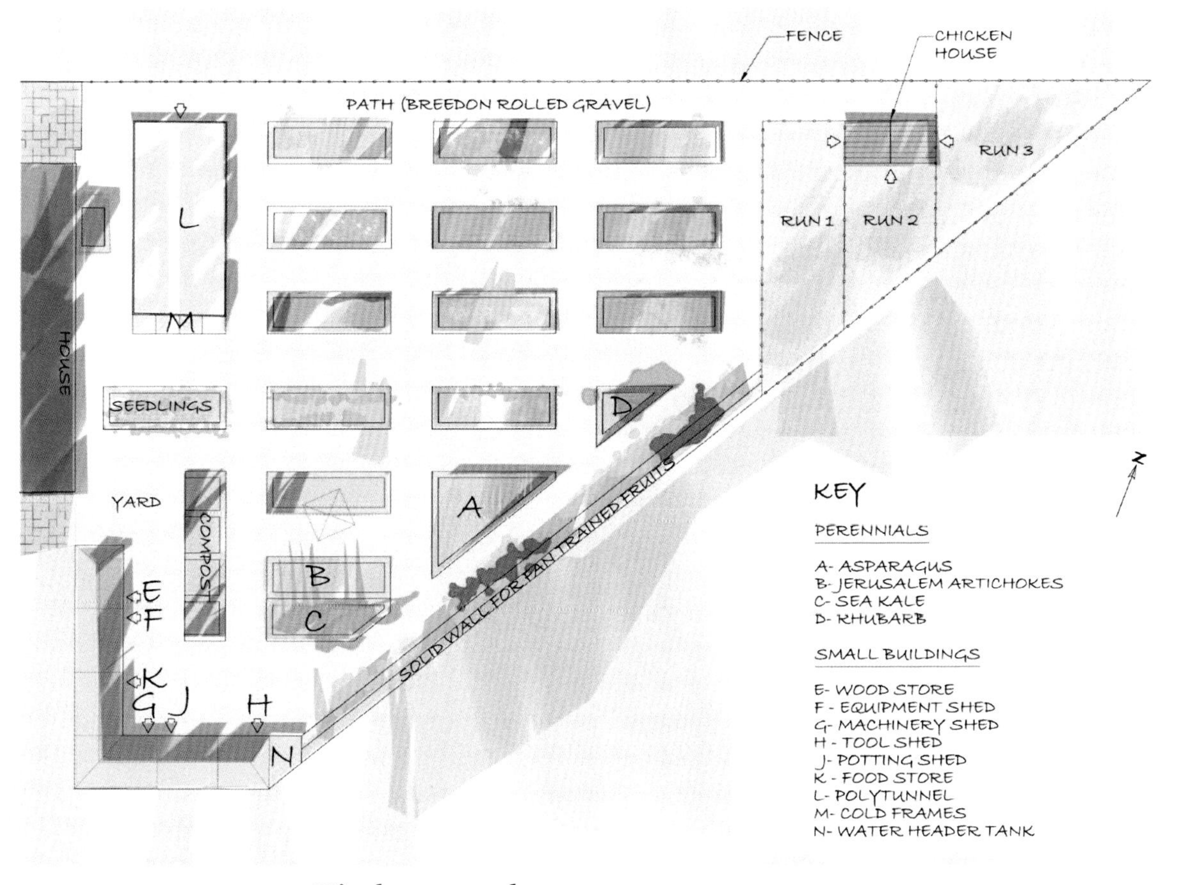

Kitchen garden area

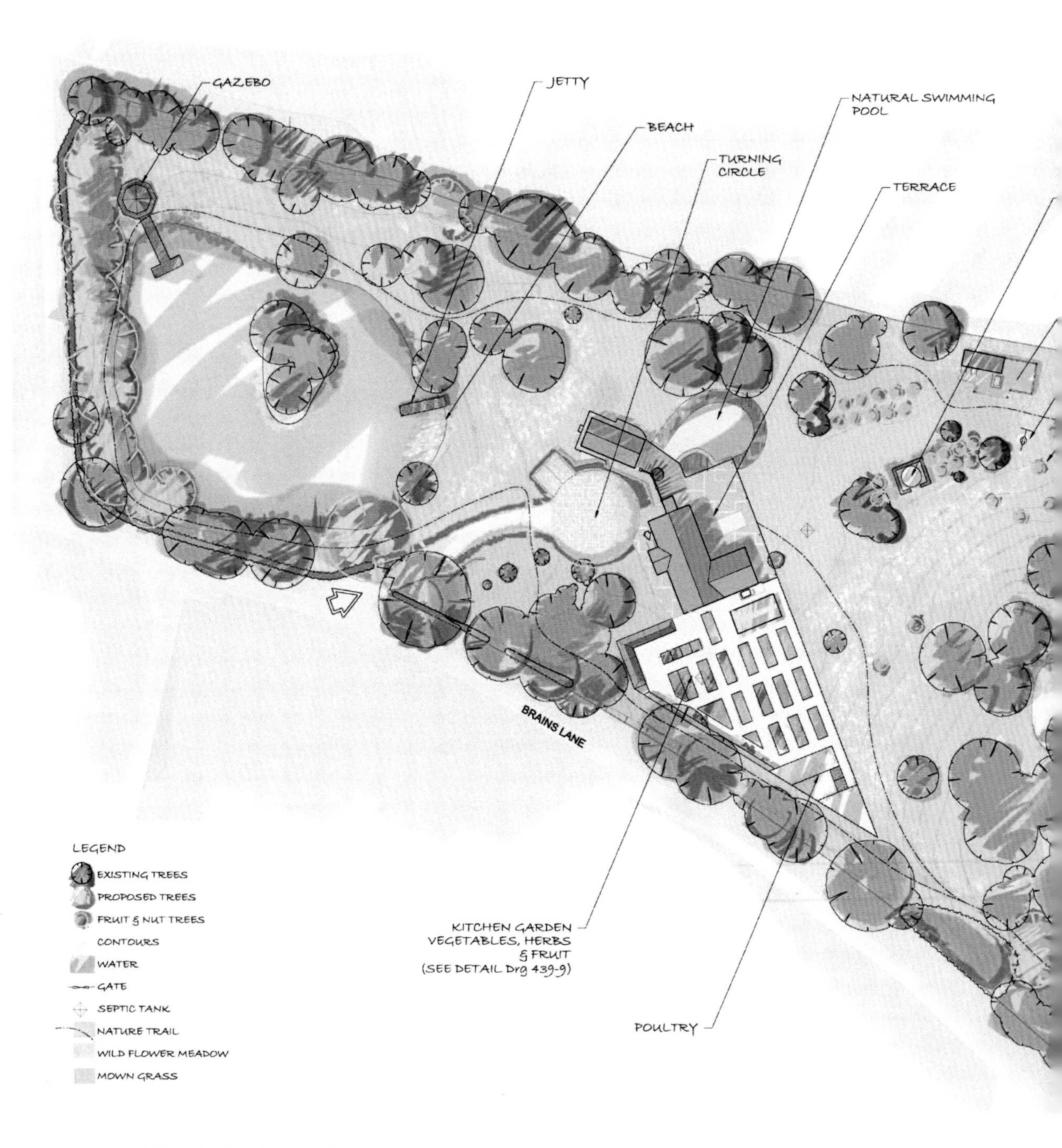

Final design plan

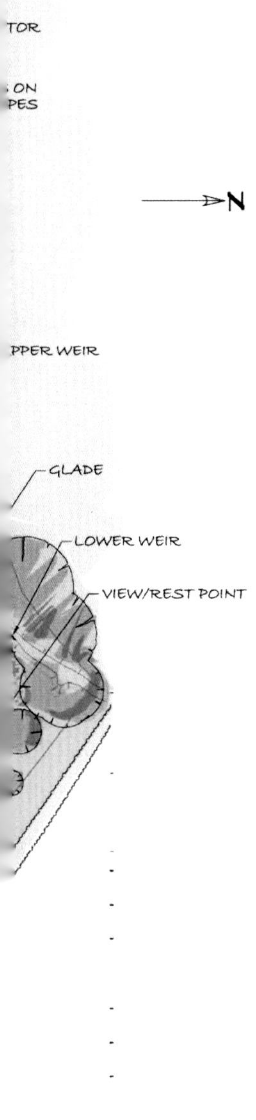

planting additional native trees to form a linear woodland between the lake and the property boundary, which would also provide some protection from the prevailing south-westerly winds, and suggested that the mown grassed areas around the lake be converted into a wildflower meadow.

Zone 3, which covers the sloping ground to the north of the property, contained a small stream on the boundary, and a pond surrounded by trees. My proposals for this area were to enlarge the pond slightly to make it more attractive, and divert the stream to flow into and out of the pond. I then suggested planting nut trees on the sloping ground, underplanted with wild flowers and grasses. The remaining area was allocated to woodland; the recommendation was for a mixture of native species including ash, hornbeam, hazel and oak, all of which would provide timber for heating and rustic building projects as well as having considerable wildlife value.

Around the boundaries of the property it was suggested that the formal cut hedgerows be replaced with woodland, approximately 4 to 6m (13 to 20ft) wide, containing as wide as possible a mixture of native trees, shrubs, wild flowers, grasses and herbs. These would become valuable biological corridors for wildlife. I also proposed creating a nature trail inside the boundaries, which would serve to link the different areas and provide a recreational and educational resource throughout the year.

The report:

These proposals formed the basis of the 40-page management plan which was created for the property. The document also included a range of plans and images, a detailed programme of work and planting lists. It will serve both as a guide for action as The Birches Smallholding is developed over the coming years, and as a permanent record of an inspiring project.

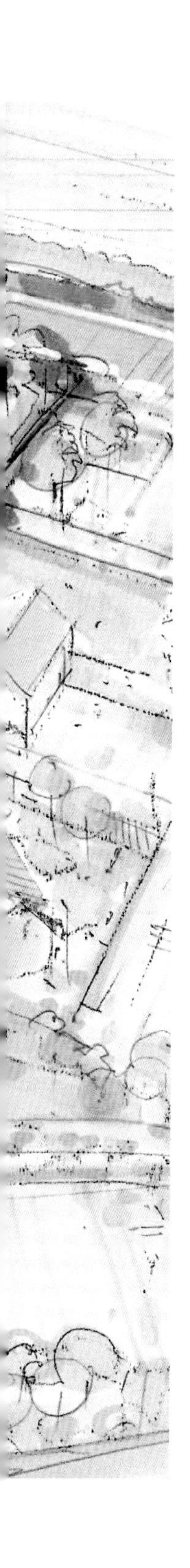

Wandale

The property:

The four-hectare (10-acre) Wandale site is part of an elevated plateau surrounded by tranquil rolling farming landscape, with a mixture of arable and grazing land contained by trimmed hedgerows. There are discrete linear woodlands scattered throughout the area, mainly to the north.

The brief:

To create a conservation plan for the landscape incorporating wetland, grassland and woodland, using native species in the interests of conservation and to create habitats for wildlife. The owners wished to consider renewable energy options, rainwater harvesting and natural waste water treatment. They wanted areas for the growing of organic food and the natural rearing of animals, and to grow trees for fuel and amenity. They also wanted to incorporate facilities for recreation.

The plan:

The existing site fell into two distinct parts: the top area of 0.75 hectares (1.9 acres), where there were disused farm buildings, areas of concrete surfacing, a gravel driveway and a large modern tractor barn; and an elongated field of 3.5 hectares (8.6 acres), sloping fairly steeply in a southerly direction. The owners' intentions were to convert the farm buildings into a house, demolish the barn, develop the top area into residential gardens and the core of their smallholding, and use the field for arable crops and grazing.

The only vegetation on the site was grass and hedges, with an occasional tree. Hedgerows formed the enclosure on the

Top area plan

eastern and western boundaries, but they were in poor condition. The site is very exposed to the elements, with the strongest winds from the north and north-east, but receives the maximum possible amount of sunshine.

In developing proposals for the site, three main 'use areas' were identified: Private, Productive and Landscape. The Private Area covers the space in front of the farm buildings and up to the boundary walls. The concrete surfacing in this area needed to be removed, and the existing concrete block wall raised to 2m (6ft 6in) to provide privacy and protection.

The courtyard between the existing U-shaped buildings (marked 'A' on the plan) was identified as the ideal spot for a natural swimming pool. Here it will not only be protected from inclement weather but also be warmer. It will form a central feature and be attractive all year round. The design identified the old yard (marked 'B') as most suitable for the vegetable garden, and I suggested that this be laid out in the form of a potager to help make this area attractive as well as functional. In this area space was also allocated for other features including a fruit cage, a seat with an arbour, screen fencing for privacy and climbing plants, and brick paving.

The Productive Area covers all the land on the plateau. This was identified as ideal for various uses associated with smallholding. I proposed the area marked 'C' as space for residents' and visitors' cars, as this is as near the main entrance to the house as possible. It is envisaged that a car port and not a garage will be built, so there is no large building causing a visual intrusion on the landscape. I suggested that the roof could be covered with wire mesh and climbing plants, which will be beneficial to wildlife and also reduce the visual impact of vehicles.

The space marked 'D' was set aside for small farm animals and poultry, with the necessary buildings and runs. The plan noted that these could be rotated to the adjacent area, marked 'F', which could alternatively be developed as a paddock for a pony. Area 'D' could also be used for growing vegetables which require more space, such as potatoes, and for perennial crops.

I suggested that a rainwater-harvesting pond be located in

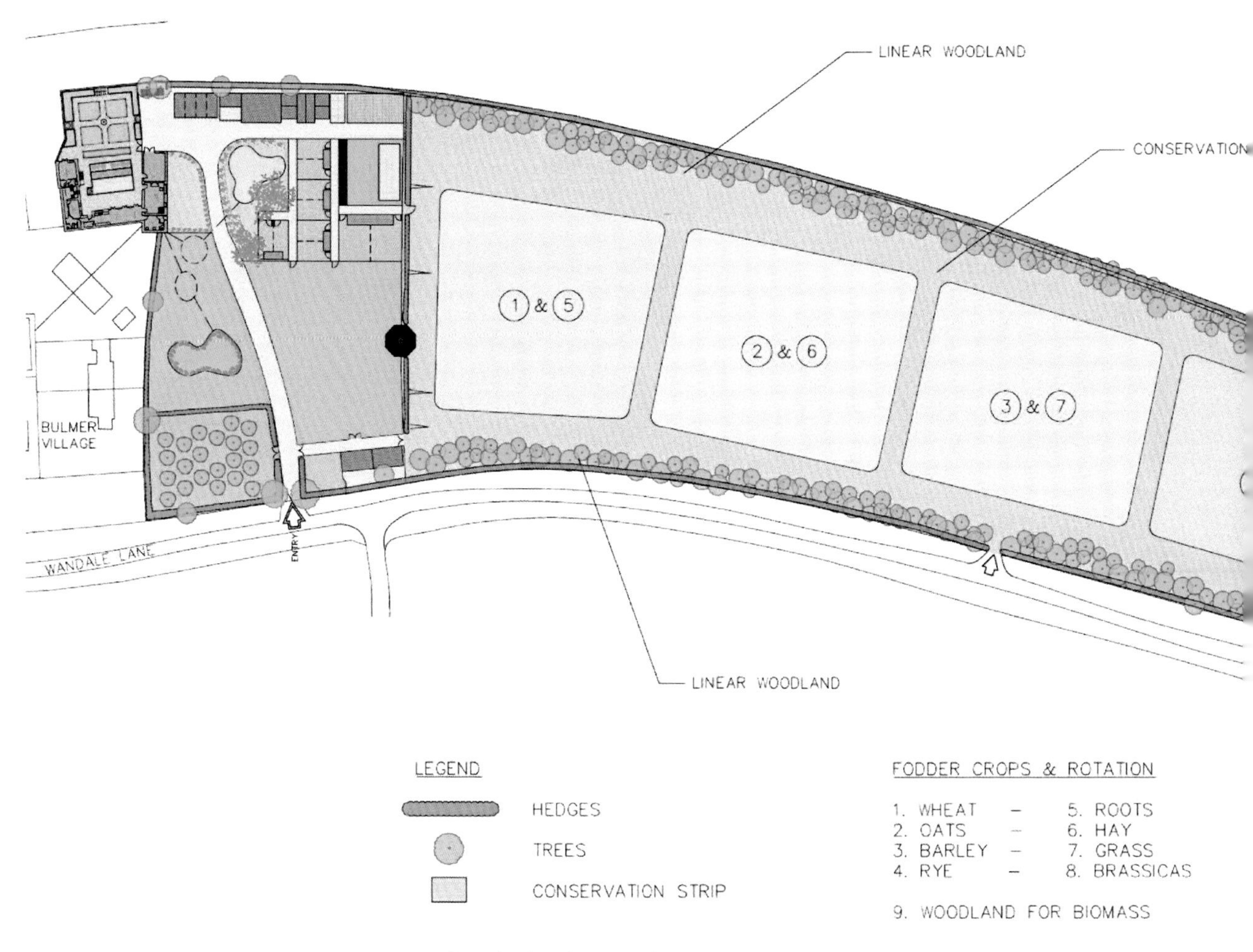

Final design plan

this area, making it conveniently near the animals and gardens. Rainwater from the roofs could be collected and stored in an underground tank and also directed to the pond. Within this area space was also allocated for small buildings such as a potting shed, equipment store, hay barn and timber store. It was proposed that any larger buildings be located on the eastern boundary to help provide protection from the prevailing winds, and that the existing hedgerows should be developed into a linear woodland along the boundaries of this area, to provide shelter and privacy. The space marked 'E' was suggested as the location for a waste water system in the form of reed ponds, and also for a small orchard.

The Landscape Area is all the land sloping from the plateau to the far end of the site. Three alterative uses were suggested for this area: it could be used for grazing animals such as sheep, or for the growing of fodder crops, or made into a wildflower meadow, which would provide good-quality hay. I proposed that a small native woodland be established at the far end of this area, and that the trees should be coppiced and thinned as part of the management to provide fuel. The plan noted that the hedges would need attention to make them much more effective for stock control, if the owners chose to keep livestock in this area. It was suggested that there should be a conservation margin around the entire area, as this would be beneficial to wildlife.

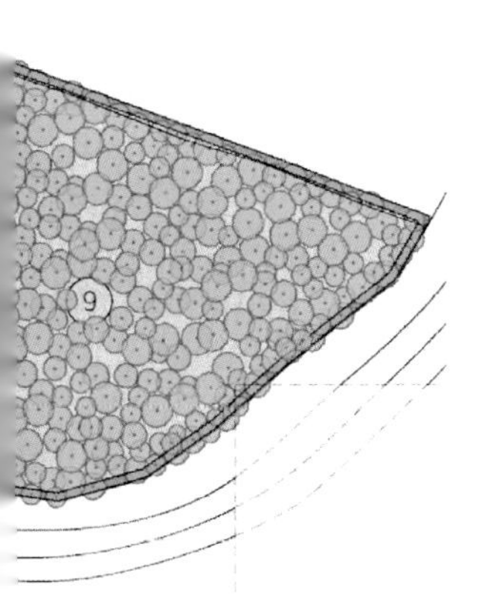

The report:

These proposals formed the basis of a 36-page management plan for the property, which also included a full implementation programme and detailed short- and long-term objectives for the management of the property. This provided the owners with a structured plan of action, enabling them to embark upon their dream of developing Wandale into an eco-smallholding.

Troutwells

The property:

Troutwells is a 0.8-hectare (two-acre) site situated on the fringes of Exmoor National Park. About half the site is on a hillside and the rest is in the valley bottom next to a stream, which is approximately 2.4m (8ft) wide as it passes through the site.

The brief:

The owners' aims were to embrace permaculture principles, conserve energy by using natural systems wherever possible, and create an attractive, functional and sustainable smallholding in harmony with nature. They wanted to maximise the use of the land for growing crops, but because they planned to continue their freelance professional work to provide an income and fund their capital projects, they did not envisage keeping any animals apart from poultry. The brief was therefore to produce a management plan for the smallholding covering all aspects of permaculture, including organics, biodynamics and the principles of sustainability. Hillside management is much more demanding than working flat land, so the design needed to take this into account.

The plan:

For planning purposes, the land was divided into three areas. The Flat Land encompassed the land between the stream and the road boundary. The Hill Land was the area from the stream to the top of the site on the south-west boundary, and the Lower Land comprised a very small area in the south-west corner of the site.

The existing site was covered with many large trees, particularly alders, willows and hazels, along both sides of the stream. Conifers and other ornamental trees and shrubs

occupied the rest of the site. All would need to be felled, the stumps removed and the ground restored in order to create land for growing and to admit light.

The Flat Land was identified as the ideal location for vegetables and herbs, both annuals and perennials, to be grown in slightly raised beds surrounded by ornamental perennials, grasses and shrubs. To increase the growing space, I suggested covering the entrance pergola to the garden area with grapes, and a gazebo with Chinese gooseberries. The design for this area included a summerhouse near the stream, as a place for the owners and visitors to use for rest and recreation. In the northern corner of the site, I proposed establishing a mini woodland for growing trees for fuel.

The plan recommended using the Hill Land for fruit and nut trees and bushes of all kinds, both native and introduced species, and suggested that these should be underplanted with perennials, herbs and companion plants to create a forest garden. The plant-raising area, incorporating two greenhouses, cold frames and raised beds, was located at the top of the Hill Land, as this received the most light and sunshine.

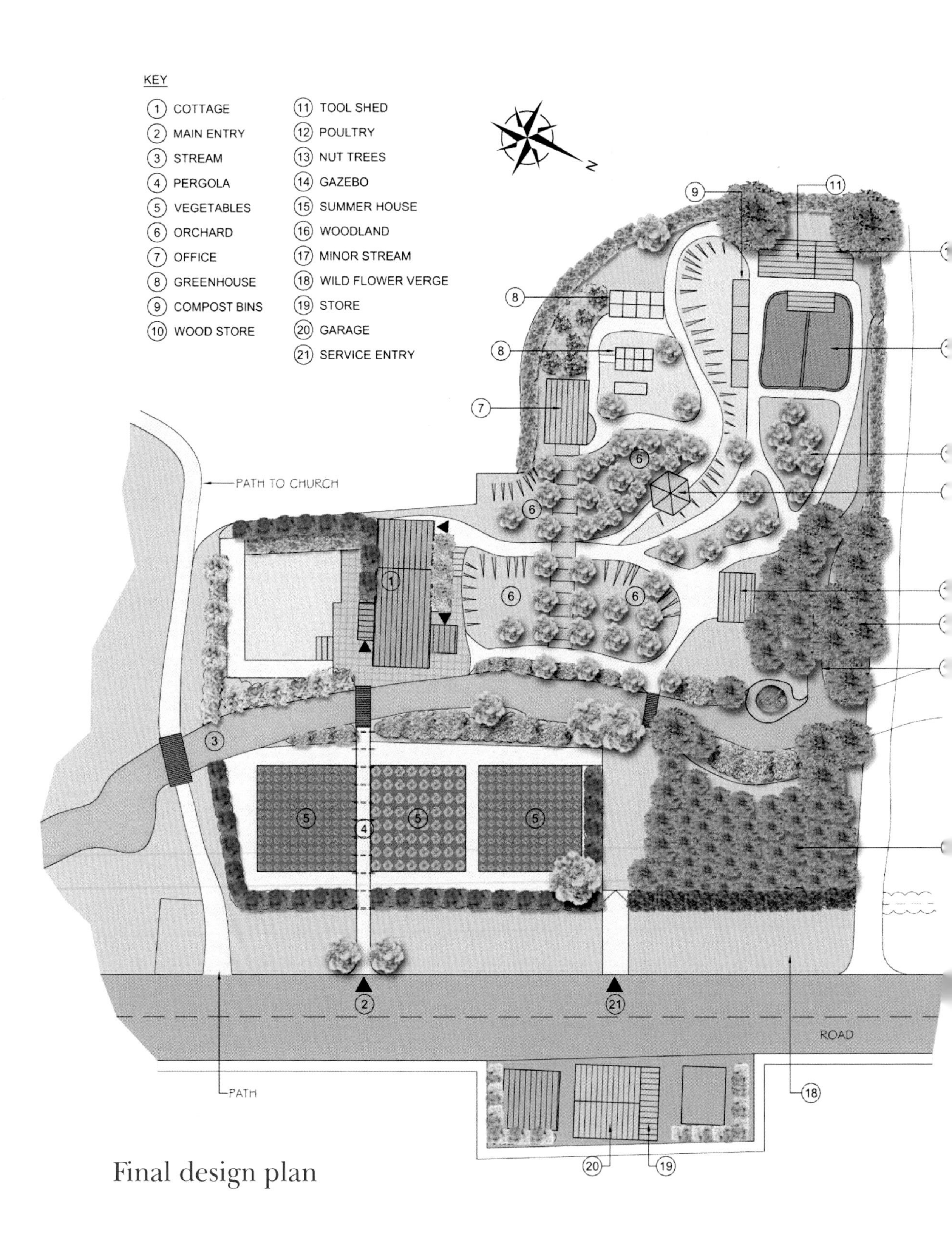

Final design plan

The Lower Land was identified as the best place for the 'service' aspects of the holding: sheds and stores for tools, equipment, firewood, hay and straw bales, wood chips and leaves. The poultry house and run would also be located in this area. Space was also planned here for four compost bins with covered roofs, and for drums for making liquid manures from comfrey, nettles and seaweed.

I proposed that all the boundaries should be enclosed by native hedgerows, and my design also included a network of paths, surfaced with scalpings to provide an all-weather surface, to link the various locations and facilities. The design also included plans to reshape the banks of the stream and add large natural stone boulders to create small waterfalls as well as pools for the trout in the stream.

The report:

The resulting management plan provided the owners with a template for a true forest garden, which would combine good design with effective practical functioning and habitats for wildlife. It allowed them to develop Troutwells into the smallholding of their dreams, where they would live in harmony with nature for the next 10 years.

APPENDICES

1 Table of landscape elements

Element	Function in farm management	Potential value in the landscape	Need and scope for enhanceme
HILLS (1) Rolling	Probably capable of cultivation	Forming horizon. Forming focal point of view. Enclosing dips and valleys between them. Inviting exploration – promising a view.	Are hills in the locality usually bare-topped? If not, may be appropriate emphasise hillcrest by planting. If y then important not to site buildings or tree-planting on the crest. If som field boundaries are to be removed, keep those which run with the contours.
HILLS (2) Isolated outcrops of different geology	May be too steep/ stony/infertile for cultivation	A focal point, or beacon; point of orientation for the traveller. Different vegetation may give texture and colour to the view.	Retain prominence – emphasise wit planting; treatment on lower slopes (e.g. planting, new buildings, etc.) should not diminish the scale of the hill.
HILLS (3) High moorland	Rough grazing; usually not capable of major improvement. Shooting.	A wild open landscape valued by walkers and naturalists; characteristically large expanses of subtly coloured vegetation.	Minimal change; requires continue low level of grazing, little drainage, fertilisers.
WATER (1) High moorland	Drainage, watering stock, irrigation	Water attracts people; water in any landscape reflects the landform, geology and climate and hence reinforces a landscape's character. The tumbling stream in a hilly upland area, or the meandering river in lowlands, helps to create the landform.	The course of a stream or river deserves emphasis as a key feature, perhaps by planting. Natural linear features could be used not merely a field boundaries but as boundaries cultivation for different crops. Whe public footpaths run close to, but d not give access to water, considerati should be given to rerouting to red the likelihood of trespass as well as enhance people's experience of the landscape.

lement	Function in farm management	Potential value in the landscape	Need and scope for enhancements
'ATER) Ponds, ditches	Drainage, watering stock, irrigation	On a small scale they are valuable features, often offering vegetational variety and contributing to pattern in the landscape (e.g. dew ponds in Derbyshire, marlpits in parts of Worcestershire).	Ponds are rarely functional; ditches may also be redundant. Visual and wildlife value is usually reduced by neglect.
RTEFACTS g. barns, windmills, eepfolds	Often redundant because of location, cost of repair or change in farming practices.	Constructed of traditional materials to perform an agricultural function suited to the soil, landform and climate, old farm buildings are valuable in providing visual evidence to the onlooker of the landscape's history. They add variety, often form focal points, and indicate a human presence (particularly important in a wild or exposed landscape). Where artefacts are virtually in ruins, they may constitute eyesores.	Where there is a historic as well as visual function, artefacts should be conserved and repaired. Where the function is largely visual, repair or at least retention is desirable, unless the item clearly is an eyesore.
RMSTEADS ND GRICULTURAL UILDINGS	Housing stock, crops, machinery; homes for farmer/workers	An integral part of the landscape character of the countryside; an important feature in all but the remotest upland areas. New buildings are often alien in size and colour, dwarfing existing barns and farmhouses. By their size they draw the eye and detract from the landscape. Buildings often emphasise an aspect of the landscape sited at a river crossing, in the shelter of a valley or in the lee of a wood, thus reinforcing the quality of shelter.	The impact of new buildings can be reduced by choice of cladding or paint colour (dark brown/grey/black rather than cream or green); breaking up the roofline, or tying it in with existing buildings, reduces the scale of large structures. A large, alien structure may be better sited away from a cluster of traditional buildings, in a fold of the landform or carefully screened.

Element	Function in farm management	Potential value in the landscape	Need and scope for enhancemer
GROUND VEGETATION	As crop or pasture, the major source of farm income, requiring intensive management.	Most farm crops are low-growing. Thus their contribution in the landscape is as colour and texture changing with the seasons. Some crops can make a dramatic impact – rape in flower, ripening corn, fruit blossom. A varied cropping pattern is more appealing visually than a monoculture, though the open landscapes of monoculture have a certain grandeur. Pasture, particularly herb-rich pasture or rough grazing, changes colour with the seasons. Grass leys and improved pasture tend to be monotonous green without seasonal change. Wild plants add vitality and colour to the landscape (e.g. scattered poppies in ripening corn evoke universal pleasure in all but the agro-farming community). The colour of an unfertilised pasture is subtle and varied and of course to the informed visitor will emphasise landscape character, because it reflects underlying geology.	On larger farms, the choice of crop and its management is governed almost entirely by economics. The scope therefore for introducing vari colour or texture as a policy for enhancement is virtually non-existe It is worth bearing in mind, howeve that where a farmer is changing thei farming pattern towards monocultu the value of other landscape feature in adding incident to the view will b greater. In conserving areas of farmland whe wild flowers can flourish, farmers wi not only be contributing to wildlife, but to the landscape's attractiveness well.
TREES (1) Isolated or in hedgerows	Shade for stock. Value as timber.	Points of reference; important vertical elements. Focal points. Indicate the scale of an open landscape – but many scattered trees may lead to a fragmented view. Trees along roads or footpaths may give welcome shade, or offer rhythm of light and shade. If related to building, emphasises settlement pattern.	Many trees are over-mature, thus th is a need for new planting, or better, encouragement of hedgerow saplin New planting should reflect and strengthen the pattern of tree planti by planting at field corners, along roads, or close to buildings as appropriate to each landscape. Where extensive scattered tree cove seems to fragment a view, new planting should be in more concentrated clumps.
TREES (2) Copse, spinney	Timber, firewood, etc. Game preservation.	Often important elements in the landscape creating contrasts of form and colour.	Usually in need of management because neglected or over-aged; coppicing and underplanting may b required.

ement	Function in farm management	Potential value in the landscape	Need and scope for enhancements
REES) Broadleaved oods	Timber, firewood, etc. Game preservation.	Major landscape elements, often drawing the eye. Large woodlands will emphasise landform. Texture and colour. Creating sense of enclosure and shelter, particularly in exposed areas. May screen eyesores.	Need regular management to survive. New planting – for shelter or for game management – should reflect the scale, composition and location of existing woodlands. Well-sited planting will enhance most landscapes.
REES) Conifer antations	Timber, firewood, etc. Game preservation. Shelter.	In upland areas the strong colour and outline of conifers can be a welcome feature in exposed landscapes, but extensive conifer plantations often appear forbidding, due to their dark colour and impenetrable quality. Where boundaries run counter to the natural landform, plantations can be eyesores. If the planting is of mixed species there is colour and some seasonal change. In lowland areas, where colour and form in the landscape are softer, conifers usually look out of place.	Where plantings have unsympathetic boundaries, extensions to soften their impact are desirable, as well as the addition of some broadleaved species. In exposed areas, well-sited plantations – avoiding hill crests, following valley lines, etc. – can add to the landscape's visual quality.
EDGES) Typically tall, or dge and bank	Stockproof fences. Shelter. Game preservation.	Create sense of enclosure for fields and lanes. Visually divide the landscape – create a 'human scale'. Add vertical emphasis (important in a flat landscape). Bring colour and seasonal change to landscape.	Retain key hedges: those of historic interest, forming strong lines in the view, enclosing lanes and paths, screening eyesores. If field enlargement is required, recommend for removal hedges which are gappy or which do not form a key part in an overall view of landscape.
EDGES) Low/vestigial	May not be stockproof. No function, but trimmed for neatness.	May divide a large-scale landscape into a more human scale. May reduce the visual integrity of large-scale landscape. May assist with screening eyesores. Give vertical emphasis. Bring colour and seasonal change to the landscape.	Hedges trimmed very low become gappy; they then fail to perform a satisfactory role in the landscape. Encourage growth of key hedges to at least 1m and plant up gaps. The removal of vestigial hedges might enhance some landscapes, by creating a grander scale.

Element	Function in farm management	Potential value in the landscape	Need and scope for enhancemer
WALLS	Stockproof fences	Emphasise landscape character and reflect underlying geology. Divide usually upland large-scale landscape. Often create strong patterns across the landscape: chequerboard or flowing lines of parallel walls. Colour contrast with vegetation.	Major maintenance problems lead t neglect; tumbledown walls rarely ha a visual function except on moors, t emphasis ruggedness and wildness. Removal should reflect the landforr and avoid destruction of strong patterns created by walls.

ANALYSIS

Consider the landscape in terms of its elements, zones and views. The table above gives examples of what to look for.

Five particular factors should help with design proposals:

Features and characteristics: Those features and landscape elements which contribute most to the landscape's distinctive character and quality. These warrant conservation and may include key hedgerows, traditional buildings, trees, woodlands, watercourses. (Distinguish between landform and land cover; that is, between the skeleton of the landscape and its flesh and clothing.)

Elements which frame views and define zones: Landscape elements which are of importance in helping define different landscape zones, but which need strengthening by new planting or a change in management – e.g. gappy hedgerows, over-mature trees to be replaced, streams without bankside planting, eye-catchers which do not stand out enough, views that need framing.

Eyesores: Eyesores requiring screening or removal or tidying. These may include vestigial hedgerows which are too far gone to plant up, buildings painted in inappropriate colours, over-sized buildings whose impact could be reduced by screening.

Scope for new features: The need for new landscap features – as focal points, or for emphasis of the landform or a watercourse, or additional tree cover reduce bleakness.

Hidden ground: Areas of the holding where future change would be least disruptive to the landscape, either because the landform offers a naturally hidd site or because the area is less visible to visitors and the public.

As well as analysing the individual elements in this way, think about why the zones and views identified have their particular characters and whether these should be conserved or ignored. A site which is not particularly attractive to look at may well be fascinating and functional because of the different qualities of different parts. In such a case it may wel be worthwhile to emphasise those differences.

Reprinted from ***"Landscape Assessment of Farmland"*** *CCP 225 by Rachel Berger for the Countryside Commission 1988. Source provider: Natural England – Historical information.*

2 Zone system contents and uses

one	Structures	Plants	Growing techniques	Water sources	Animals	Human uses
ONE 1 ost visited; tensive use ıd care	house, garage, greenhouse, trellis, arbour, deck, patio, household storage, workshop, farmstead	vegetables, fruit, herbs, flowers, dwarf trees, low shrubs, lawn	intensive weeding and mulching, companion/ moon planting	rain tanks, small ponds, grey water, household tap	wild birds, rabbits, guinea pigs	modification of house microclimate, daily food and flowers, social space
ONE 2 mi- tensely ltivated	greenhouse, barns, sheds, workshop, wood storage, equipment/ machinery storage	crops for storage and freezing, small orchards	mulching, cover crops, seasonal pruning, composting, manuring	well, pond, grey water, irrigation, swales, waste water treatment ponds	rabbits, fish, poultry, soil organisms, beneficial insects	food production, market crops, plant propagation, wildlife habitats
ONE 3 rm zone	feed storage, field shelters	cash crops, large fruit and nut trees, animal forage, fodder crops, shelter belts, seedlings for grafting	cover crops, limited pruning, moveable fences	large ponds, swales, storage in soil	larger poultry, pigs, sheep, goats, cows, other smaller animals, soil organisms, beneficial insects	arable crops, firewood and timber, grazing
ONE 4 nimal care	animal feeders, bird hides	woodland, timber, native plants	grazing, selective woodland	ponds, swales	large animals, soil organisms, beneficial insects	gathering, grazing
ONE 5 ld; managed	bench seats for observation, bird hides	native plants, natural landscape	unmanaged scrub, coppice wood	lakes, streams	native animals	inspiration, foraging, meditation, wildlife watching

Adapted from original in *A Guide to Home-Scale Permaculture* by Toby Hemenway, Chelsea Green, 2009

APPENDIX 3

The Eco-Smallholding Habitats for Wild

MIXED FARMING

Small-holdings with a variety of crops, livestock and pasture can benefit farmland birds by providing safe nesting, summer food and winter food resources. They can also provide for a wide variety of mammals, insects and plants, some of which, like brown hare, require different habitats at different stages of the year. Losing one component of this mixed farming system can cause problems for farm wildlife, which is why small holdings can be so beneficial. Organic farms can often provide the mixture of crops and grassland vital to farmland birds, but conventional farming practices can be equally effective with careful thought.

FARM BUILDINGS

Old farm buildings often provide breeding or roost sites for birds and bats throughout the year. Barn owls will nest on large ledges, swallows nest on smaller ledges and beams and spotted-flycatchers will nest on ivy-clad walls. Newer buildings can also provide homes where nesting opportunities are incorporated as nestboxes are readily used by a number of species traditionally associated with barns and buildings.

STUBBLES

Cereal stubbles, particularly those associated with spring cropping, attract feeding flocks of finches, buntings and larks. The most beneficial stubbles are those left to green up with arable plants as they provide an important seed source for birds and mammals during the winter. Leaving longer stubble can provide overwintering habitat for a number of beneficial insect species.

SPRING CEREAL

Spring-sown crops are valuable as nesting and feeding habitat for birds like skylark and corn bunting. Crops sown before February often become too tall and dense by the time most ground nesting birds start breeding. Leaving spring sown cereals as over wintered stubbles provides additional benefits for wildlife.

CONSERVATION HEADLANDS

Farmland birds like grey partridges and corn bunting will nest in the outer edges (around 25-50m) of the crop and forage across the whole field. Limiting pesticide inputs to the outer 25-50m of a crop improves the breeding productivity of the birds, particularly where arable plants such as fumitory and field pansy are allowed to grow amongst the crop, as they provide both seed and insect food.

CULTIVATED MARGINS

Margins cultivated and left unsown and untreated by pesticides ar
be extremely important for arable plants, some of which are now v
like pheasants eye and corn marigold are limited to small pocke
hugely from well managed cultivated margins. It's important to c
when placing a cultivated margin, as lighter soils are much more
Heavy soils are much less suitable. During the winter the margir
food for birds and overwintering habitat for insects. During the
provide an important food source for pollinating insects like bees.

WILD BIRD SEED MIXTURES

Over winter survival of seed eating farmland birds is affected by the
period between late February and early April, where naturally occur
are difficult to find. Sowing blocks of mixed crops designed to seed
be hugely beneficial. Ideally a mix will be a spring sown mixtur
including cereals, millet, quinoa and kale. As kale seeds in the s
mixtures generally need replacing every two years.

BEETLE BANKS

These are grass ridges across large arable fields. They can support a
species, including beneficial insect populations and small mammal
provide foraging habitat for birds like barn owl. Where the beetle b
densely grassed over they can provide feeding and nesting habitat fo

FALLOW AREAS

In a mixed small holding system it is sometimes necessary to le
fallow to allow the land to rest. These summer fallows, when not
grass-legume ley, can provide valuable nesting habitat for s
rotavation in early March provides the bare earth that lapwing
and the slow natural growth of arable plants and grass provides
food for species like skylark. The plants also provide insect food wh
for lapwing chick food.

PERMANENT GRASS MARGINS

A network of grass margins around the farm is good for a number
provide habitat for small mammals, nesting and foraging habi
birds and habitat for beneficial insects. They also provide some res
if they are wide enough, lessening soil run off in arable fields
ditches and hedgerows from spray drift and fertiliser inputs. Ma
forming grasses, e.g. cocksfoot, help prevent problem weeds re
and shelter predatory invertebrates. These can move up to 200m i

ı aphids. Margins of finer grasses and herbs will support different
:ting regime of the margin will impact on how effective it is. Ideally
gin will be cut every three years to prevent scrub encroaching into
owever cutting the half of the margin closest to the crop every two
ore diverse structure. Ideally half the inner margins in a field would
ır and the other the following year to ensure maximum diversity

GRASS

idors alongside field edges, rivers, ditches and woodland will
ıabitat for short-tailed vole, the favoured prey of barn owls. Cut
rnate years after July to ensure that some rough grass is always
farm.

G MANAGEMENT FOR HAY AGE MEADOWS

in particular provide excellent habitat for ground nesting birds,
nanagement is sometimes detrimental to later broods. Where
a hay meadow after the 15th July will provide the best chances for
birds and protect leverets which will also use hay meadows. If a hay
icularly species rich, it will be beneficial to the plants to cut half the
e. If this is necessary, alternating the half cut each year will protect
ıness of the meadow and provide nesting and refuge habitat for
age meadows are less species rich as a rule and can take up to three
o make the cutting as wildlife friendly as possible delay the first cut
ible and leave at least six weeks between cuts to allow ground-
.g. skylark, to fledge their young. Strips and corners left uncut until
a refuge for invertebrates and nesting habitat for birds.

RICH GRASSLAND

rassland has a diverse sward of wildflowers and grasses. This
insects and provides food for birds, bats and other wildlife. Old
not be re-seeded or fertilised but managed by grazing without
. Remove or restrict grazing during breeding season if ground-
sent.

TURES

farmland are vital for wildlife, as water can be difficult to access
rming system, even a small holding. Retaining and maintaining
is important, as they are often the only easily accessible source of
nds with healthy marginal vegetation are particularly important.
Management of these features should be very light touch wherever possible. Creating new ponds, either permanent or seasonal, is helpful and placing them near to existing features enhances the value of the new pond and the older one

WOODLAND

Native species support more insects than non-natives; oaks, willows and birches are particularly rich in invertebrates. Old trees and dead wood are an important component of woodlands, providing nesting and roosting opportunities for birds and bats, and supporting a large number of deadwood specialists. Woodland rides and shrubby edges are valuable for ground flora and some species of butterfly. Maintaining management of woodlands is valuable for wildlife, particularly where it has been historically coppiced.

SCRUB

Patches of scrub can support a rich array of small insects that in turn provide food for birds and small mammals. Scrub is an important nesting habitat for linnets and whitethroats. Scrub is often overlooked or left to its own devices, but it does need to be managed. Cut small blocks in rotation to provide a mosaic of ages. Sunny edges of scrub are where most wildlife thrives and it is best to create sinuous rather than straight edges. In grassland with low wildlife value, encourage small pockets of scrub to develop.

HEDGES

Hedgerows, especially if thick and with wide bases, provide food and shelter for many species. Different birds require different sorts of hedges, e.g. bullfinches and turtle doves prefer tall hedgerows (<4m) with lots of trees, whereas linnets and yellowhammers favour shorter hedges (2-3m) with few trees. Any cutting must take place outside the nesting season and must not be undertaken before the before the 1st September or after the 1st March. Leaving the cutting to the end of winter will leave the fruits and nuts longer, and provide an over winter food source for birds and mammals. Flowering and subsequent fruiting takes place on second year growth so hedges should be cut twice in five years and on rotation.

MATURE TREES

Hedgerow trees provide habitat for some bird species, but they are particularly important for bats. Retain hedgerow trees and allow new standards to grow as replacements. Old trees with holes and dead wood provide nesting sites for birds such as little owls and tree sparrows, and provide roosting habitat for bats. In field trees are also important and often provide stepping stones between woodland blocks.

Sarah Blyth, Land Management Advisor RSPB (text); Mark Lewis (photograph); David Calow (Artwork)

4 Ecology illustrated

Reproduced from the *Oxford Reference Dictionary*, 1986, by kind permission of Oxford University Press

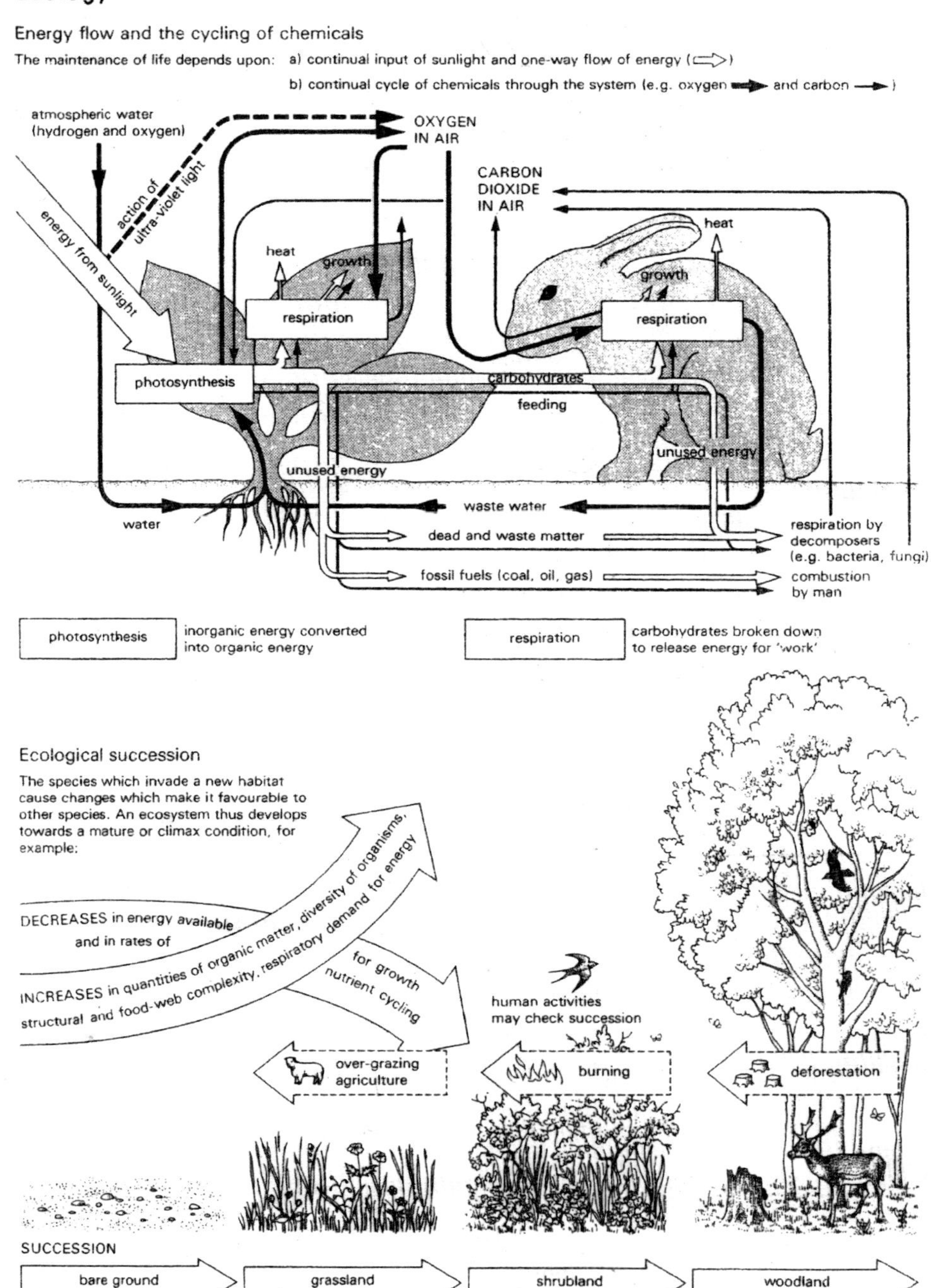

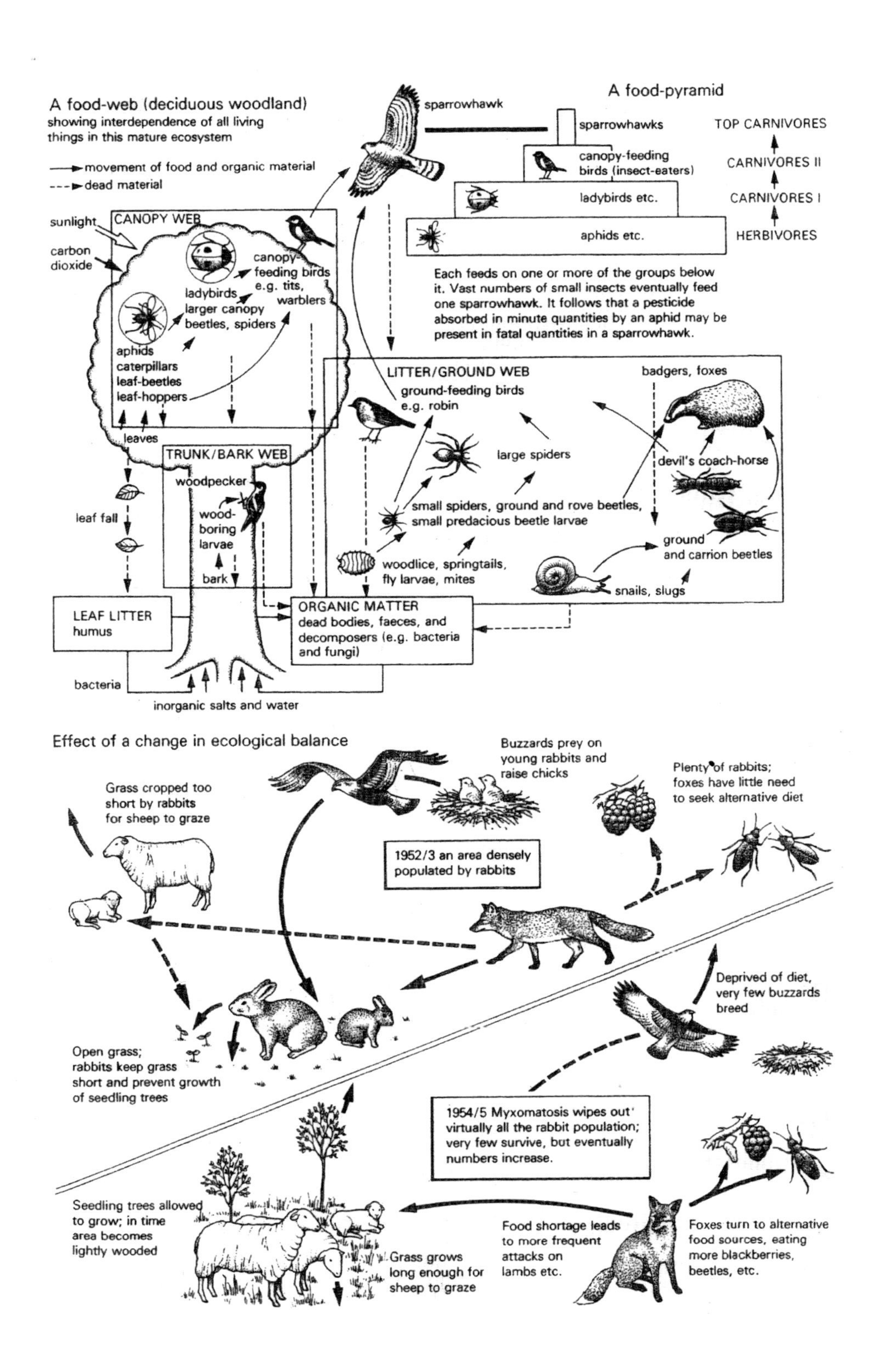
A food-web (deciduous woodland)
showing interdependence of all living things in this mature ecosystem
movement of food and organic material
dead material
sparrowhawk
A food-pyramid
sparrowhawks
TOP CARNIVORES
canopy-feeding birds (insect-eaters)
CARNIVORES II
ladybirds etc.
CARNIVORES I
aphids etc.
HERBIVORES
Each feeds on one or more of the groups below it. Vast numbers of small insects eventually feed one sparrowhawk. It follows that a pesticide absorbed in minute quantities by an aphid may be present in fatal quantities in a sparrowhawk.
sunlight
carbon dioxide
CANOPY WEB
canopy-feeding birds e.g. tits, warblers
ladybirds larger canopy beetles, spiders
aphids
caterpillars
leaf-beetles
leaf-hoppers
leaves
TRUNK/BARK WEB
woodpecker
wood-boring larvae
bark
leaf fall
LEAF LITTER
humus
bacteria
inorganic salts and water
ORGANIC MATTER
dead bodies, faeces, and decomposers (e.g. bacteria and fungi)
LITTER/GROUND WEB
ground-feeding birds e.g. robin
badgers, foxes
large spiders
devil's coach-horse
small spiders, ground and rove beetles, small predacious beetle larvae
ground and carrion beetles
woodlice, springtails, fly larvae, mites
snails, slugs
Effect of a change in ecological balance
Buzzards prey on young rabbits and raise chicks
Plenty of rabbits; foxes have little need to seek alternative diet
Grass cropped too short by rabbits for sheep to graze
1952/3 an area densely populated by rabbits
Open grass; rabbits keep grass short and prevent growth of seedling trees
Deprived of diet, very few buzzards breed
1954/5 Myxomatosis wipes out virtually all the rabbit population; very few survive, but eventually numbers increase.
Seedling trees allowed to grow; in time area becomes lightly wooded
Grass grows long enough for sheep to graze
Food shortage leads to more frequent attacks on lambs etc.
Foxes turn to alternative food sources, eating more blackberries, beetles, etc.

INFORMATION

Further reading

Books

Terry Bridge, *A Practical Guide to Self-Sufficiency*, Regency, 2012

R. W. Brunskill, *Traditional Farm Buildings of Britain and their Conservation*, Yale University Press, 2007 (originally published 1982)

Andy and Dave Hamilton, *The Self-Sufficient-Ish Bible*, Hodder & Stoughton, 2009

Toby Hemenway, *A Guide to Home-Scale Permaculture*, Chelsea Green Publishing, 2009

Paul Heiney, *Home Farm*, Dorling Kindersley, 1998

Nick Rosen, *How to Live Off-Grid*, Bantam, 2007

John Seymour, *The Fat of the Land*, Carningli Books, 2008 (originally published 1961)

John Seymour, *The Lore of the Land*, The Good Life Press, 2012 (originally published 1982)

John Seymour and Will Sutherland, *The New Complete Book of Self-Sufficiency*, Dorling Kindersley, 2003 (originally published in 1976 as *The Complete Book of Self-Sufficiency*)

Tim and Dot Tyne, *Viable Self-Sufficiency*, Home Farmer, 2016

Many other books on smallholding are available, including older titles which can be obtained from second-hand suppliers.

Magazines

Country Smallholding: **www.countrysmallholding.com**

Home Farmer: **www.homefarmer.co.uk**

Smallholder: **www.smallholder.co.uk**

Online resources

'A Farmer's Guide to the Planning System' – available as a free download from **www.gov.uk/government/uploads/system/uploads/attachment_data/file/7656/143516.pdf**

Also see: **www.planningportal.gov.uk/permission/commonprojects**

Resources

Department for Environment, Food and Rural Affairs (DEFRA): **www.gov.uk/government/organisations/department-for-environment-food-rural-affairs**

Welsh Government Environment and Countryside: **www.gov.wales/topics/environmentcountryside**

The Scottish Government Farming and Rural Affairs: **www.gov.scot/agri**

Northern Ireland Department of Agriculture, Environment and Rural Affairs: **www.daera-ni.gov.uk**

Agricultural Development and Advisory Service (ADAS): **www.adas.uk**

Linking Environment and Farming (LEAF): **www.leafuk.org**

Farming and Wildlife Advisory Group: **www.fwag.org.uk**

Natural England: **www.gov.uk/government/organisations/natural-england**

Natural Resources Wales: **www.naturalresources.wales**

Scottish Natural Heritage: **www.snh.gov.uk**

Forestry Commission: **www.forestry.gov.uk**

Soil Association: **www.soilassociation.org**

Garden Organic: **www.gardenorganic.org.uk**

The Conservation Volunteers (formerly British Trust for Conservation Volunteers): **www.tcv.org.uk**

The Wildlife Trusts: **www.wildlifetrusts.org**

Royal Society for the Protection of Birds: **www.rspb.org.uk**

Ordnance Survey: **www.ordnancesurvey.co.uk**

There are many local smallholding associations, details of which can be found online.

Acknowledgements

Manuscript

My sincere thanks to the following people who kindly read my draft manuscript and provided many helpful and useful comments:

Geoff Aucock, smallholder

Andrew Porter, smallholder

Graham Smith, editor

Benedict Vanheems, gardening and wildlife writer

Eva Venny, smallholder

The late Patrick Whitefield, permaculture designer

Book production

I am very grateful to the following people who have made this book possible through their expertise and their willingness to assist me:

Gaby Bartai: Editor

Sarah Blyth: Wildlife adviser

Andrew Crane: Graphic designer

Kat Khan-Davis: Secretary

SKETCHES

David Calow

DRAWINGS

Tom Evans, Ian Osman and Kate Wood

PHOTOGRAPHIC IMAGES

Penny Bunting, Mark Lewis and Simon McEwen

MAPS

All O.S. Maps – pages 39/66/106 – Crown copyright © 2009

Ordnance Survey Licence Number 100058011

Conversion tables

	Metric	Imperial
Length	1 millimetre (mm)	0.0394 in
	1 centimetre (cm)/10mm	0.3937 in
	1 metre/100cm	39.37 in/3.281 ft/1.094 yd
	1 kilometre (km) 1000 metres	1093.6 yd/0.6214 mile
	25.4mm/2.54cm	1 inch
	304.8mm/30.48cm/0.3048m	1 foot (ft) 12in
	914.4mm/91.44cm/0.9144m	1 yard (yd) 3ft
	1609.344 metres/1.609km	1 mile/1760 yd
Area	1 square centimetre (sq cm)/ 100 sq millimetres (sq mm)	0.155 sq in
	1 square metre (sq m)/10,000 sq cm	10.764 sq ft/1.196 sq yd
	1 are/100 sq metres	119.60 sq yd/0.0247 acre
	1 hectare (ha)/100 ares	2.471 acres/0.00386 sq mile
	645.16 sq mm/6.4516 sq cm	1 square inch (sq in)
	929.03 sq cm	1 square foot (sq ft) 144 sq in
	8361.3 sq cm/0.8361 sq m	1 square yard (sq yd)/9 sq ft
	4046.9 sq m/0.4047 ha	1 acre/4840 sq yd
	259 ha/2.59 sq km	1 square mile/640 acres
Volume	1 cubic centimetre (cu cm)/ 10000 cubic millimetres (cu mm)	0.0610 cu in
	1 cubic decimetre (cu dm)/1000 cu cm	61.024 cu in/0.0353 cu ft
	1 cubic metre/1000 cu dm	35.3147 cu ft/1.308 cu yd
	1 cu cm = 1 millilitre (ml)	
	1 cu dm = 1 litre (see Capacity)	
	16.3871 cu cm	1 cubic inch (cu in)
	28,316.8 cu cm/0.0283 cu metre	1 cubic foot (cu ft)/1728 cu in
	0.7646 cu metre	1 cubic yard (cu yd)/27 cu ft
Capacity	1 litre	1.7598 pt/0.8799 qt/0.22 gal
	0.568 litre	1 pint (pt)
	1.137 litres	1 quart (qt)
	4.546 litres	1 gallon (gal)
	1 gram(g)	0.035 oz
	1 kilogram (kg)/1000 g	2.20 lb/35.2 oz
	1 tonne/1000 kg	2204.6 lb/0.9842 ton
	28.35 g	1 ounce (oz)
	0.4536 kg	1 pound (lb)
	1016 kg	1 ton
Weight	1 gram per square metre (g/metre^2)	0.0295 oz/sq yd
	1 gram per square centimetre (g/cm^2)	0.228 oz/sq in
	1 kilogram per square centimetre (kg/cm^2)	14.223 lb/sq in
	1 kilogram per square metre (kg/metre^2)	0.205 lb/sq ft
Temperature	To convert °F to °C, subtract 32, then divide by 9 and multiply by 5	
	To convert °C to °F, divide by 5 and multiply by 9, then add 32	

About the author

Michael Littlewood is a natural landscape architect and environmental planner with extensive experience of designing and implementing sustainable land use projects. His mission has been the introduction of ecological design and planning into the mainstream.

His reputation derives from work over many years in the UK, Australia, New Zealand, Saudi Arabia, Malaysia, Greece and Portugal, in a wide variety of situations, landscapes and climates. His clients have included national, regional and local governments, universities, colleges and schools, landowners and developers, and the owners of farms, smallholdings, estates and gardens.

His designs incorporate his specialisms of eco-building, bio-engineering, renewable energy systems, natural waste treatments, water harvesting, organic food production, wildlife and nature conservation, and natural swimming pools (which he introduced to the UK). This enables him to give his clients not just the landscape amenities they require for the present but also an improved environment for the future.

Michael is the author of many other publications. He has produced a range of books, posters and calendars on organic gardening, a series of books on natural swimming pools, four technical books on landscape detailing, and a series of brochures covering his concepts of the sustainable village, farm, school and residence.

He has extensive teaching experience at universities and colleges in the UK and abroad, and has owned smallholdings in England and New Zealand.

In his work Michael has been guided by a belief in the necessity and value of working in harmony with nature. This has led him to a philosophy and design approach rooted in the permaculture ethics of integrating earth care with people care to the increased benefit of both. He sees his concepts as a dramatic and conspicuous example of the value of ecological design, where separating and combining functions and uses makes the best of both worlds, the natural and the artificial, while at the same time creating beauty.

Visit **www.ecodesignscape.co.uk** for full details of his planning and design services and publications.